# MANAGEMENT OF CONCRETE STRUCTURES FOR LONG-TERM SERVICEABILITY

Proceedings of the International Seminar
held at the University of Sheffield, England, UK
on 13 November 1997

**Edited by :**

**Dr Ewan A Byars**
BCA Lecturer in Concrete Technology,
Centre for Cement and Concrete, University of Sheffield

and

**Dr Tony McNulty**
HM Inspector of Nuclear Installations, Health and Safety Executive

HSE

THE INSTITUTION OF
CIVIL ENGINEERS

THE INSTITUTION OF
STRUCTURAL ENGINEERS

**British Energy**

Published for the Centre for Cement and Concrete by Thomas Telford Publishing, Thomas Telford Services Ltd, 1 Heron Quay, London E14 4JD. URL: http://www.t-telford.co.uk

Distributors for Thomas Telford books are
*USA:* American Society of Civil Engineers, Publications Sales Department, 345 East 47th Street, New York, NY 10017-2398
*Japan:* Maruzen Co. Ltd, Book Department, 3–10 Nihonbashi 2-chome, Chuo-ku, Tokyo 103
*Australia:* DA Books and Journals, 648 Whitehorse Road, Mitcham 3132, Victoria

First published 1997

*Cover photograph:* Sizewell B Power Station
©Nuclear Electric

A catalogue record for this book is available from the British Library

ISBN: 0 7277 2654 4

Printed and bound in Great Britain by Bookcraft (Bath) Ltd

# Preface

Concrete is the principal choice of material for the construction of large civil engineering structures. The developed world has demonstrated its faith in the material by choosing concrete for the main structures of industrial and chemical plant as well as for transport, water and energy-related infrastructures. The capital cost of these assets is such that replacement is expensive and, in many circumstances, not a valid option. Thus structural concrete plays an important role in the economic and social fabric of many nations and is required to perform its function with integrity and reliability for decades and possibly centuries in the case of nuclear safety-related structures.

As clients, architects, engineers, contractors and users we are all responsible for ensuring that concrete structures are designed, constructed and managed in a way that ensures serviceability over their projected life. However, this has to be achieved within the constraints of increased competitiveness within the international marketplace.

Maintaining a concrete structure at an appropriate level of serviceability throughout its life relies upon the development of effective strategies for managing ageing. These strategies must be supported by validated predictive and inspection techniques for quantifying the effects of ageing at both the material and structural levels.

Current construction contracts contain only a nominal measure of maintenance requirement. Furthermore, assurance of through-life structural integrity is not necessarily supported by long-term strategies for serviceability in terms of design, construction, prediction, inspection, management or monitoring techniques.

The central theme of this International Seminar is Management of Concrete Structures for Long-Term Serviceability. Sub-theme one, *Design, Construction, Prediction and Inspection* examines current developments in national and international codes and standards, international research initiatives, design considerations for durable concrete, emerging predictive techniques and inspection and assessment of safety-critical concrete structures. Sub-theme 2, *Strategies for Maintenance and Serviceability*, identifies the main considerations for developing a management scheme for assuring service life of concrete structures. Also presented is an international perspective of ageing management in safety-critical nuclear structures, a strategy for replacement of concrete structures without disruption to production and case studies on the application of serviceability strategies.

The Centre for Cement and Concrete (CCC) at the University of Sheffield, UK organised this International Seminar, sponsored by the Health and Safety Executive and British Energy and the welcome support of the Institution of Civil Engineers and the Institution of Structural Engineers.

The efforts of the Organising and Scientific Committees in the preparation of the Seminar are gratefully acknowledged. The paper Authors are also thanked for their sterling and timely work in preparing the papers.

*Dr Ewan Byars and Dr Tony McNulty, October 1997*

## Organising Committee

Dr Ewan Byars (Chair)
*CCC, University of Sheffield*

Dr Michael Johnston
*Scottish Nuclear Ltd*

Dr Tony McNulty
*Health & Safety Executive*

Dr K Pilakoutas
*CCC, University of Sheffield*

Mr Steve Rogers
*Nuclear Electric Ltd*

## Scientific Committee

Dr Ewan Byars
*CCC, University of Sheffield*

Dr Michael Johnston
*Scottish Nuclear Ltd*

Dr Paul Lambert
*Mott MacDonald*

Dr Tony McNulty
*Health & Safety Executive*

Professor John Menzies
*Engineering Consultant*

Dr Kypros Pilakoutas
*CCC, University of Sheffield*

Mr Steve Rogers
*Nuclear Electric Ltd*

Professor Peter Waldron (Chair)
*CCC, University of Sheffield*

## Sponsoring Organisations

British Energy

Health and Safety Executive

## Supporting Organisations

Institution of Civil Engineers

Institution of Structural Engineers

# CONTENTS

# The Consequences of Poor Serviceability - and the Way Forward

BRIAN S. NEALE CEng, FIStructE, MICE
Head of Structural, Highways and Demolition Engineering, Directorate of Science & Technology, Health and Safety Executive

## SYNOPSIS

This paper discusses the consequences of poor serviceability by discussing various types of serviceability and then concentrating on catastrophic structural serviceability failure which is often catastrophic. The likelihood and consequences of failure are discussed and put into the context of risk assessment and knowledge bases. Strategy issues are dealt with rather than detailed technical issues. The reasons for poor serviceability are examined.

The Institution of Structural Engineers has a definition for structural engineering and this is examined to see if it should be augmented to take into account durability and serviceability of structures. The paper concludes by discussing possible ways forward.

## OBJECTIVES

The objectives of this paper are to give an overview of critical issues affecting the serviceability of structures, including those of concrete, with the purpose of helping:

- to stimulate further detailed discussion so that the already present generally good delivery to clients of concrete structures is enhanced still further to enable more realistic long-term safety and operating costs to be appreciated when new projects are commissioned;
- researchers and practitioners examine the current methods of dealing with client briefs;
- ways of assessing the current reliability, durability and serviceability of existing structures;
- encouraging suitable competencies through appropriate education and continuing professional development.

## INTRODUCTION

Concrete is a structural medium used to help perform a function. There are many structural mediums and many functions. The principles applied to these functions and their structures or buildings apply in general across many structural mediums. Concrete does however bring with it a number of considerations which make it susceptible to long-term serviceability. We are still learning. It has traditionally been seen as a bulk material to act in its own right, or together with reinforcement, which is usually steel of some kind. The technology of the concrete must

*Management of concrete structures for long-term serviceability.* Thomas Telford, London, 1997

be important, and this is to be discussed in detail by others in this symposium.  Concrete is only, after all, just one part of the structural system and mechanisms.

In addition to looking into the scientific and technological aspects of the various aspects of concrete, time should be taken to look also at the social economic environment as well as the physical environment in which these structures are created and are to be used.

With the development of the *Constructing the team* approach promulgated by Sir Michael Latham in 1994[1] the need to integrate the soft systems as well as the hard systems is brought to the fore.  The competencies of all who are involved including the competencies of designers, managers, operatives and researchers is important.  Together it should be possible to enable a high consistency of concrete structure to be created which is commensurate with the requirements of the client by encompassing a safe economic structure for the length of time required.

It would be easy to give this keynote address in a non positive way, but this is not my intention.   I understand however that seeing one or two catastrophic results of poor serviceability always raises the consciousness of anybody with an interest in safe structures - and that really should be everyone.   Serviceability failures could of course range from, say, staining to catastrophic. This paper will, however tend towards the structural failure end of the poor serviceability spectrum, some of which are catastrophic.

The positive messages for us as a profession are to build on any such failure to see what can be learned for the future with a view to avoiding a repeat incident and at the same time enhance further public, and clients, confidence in our the profession.

## WHAT IS SERVICEABILITY?

What does serviceability mean.  It can mean different things to different people and has been the subject of previous discussions elsewhere.  I suggest four serviceability states or categories, each of which needs to be considered for both the whole, and parts of, a premises or facility. The four states, with simplified descriptions, could be seen as:

| 1 | Structural integrity: | a built environment, both internally and externally, both micro and macro, which will resist loads safely, including self weight. |
| 2 | Aesthetic fashion: | the look and feel which complements the users desired image. |
| 3 | Fiscal maintenance: | the cost of upkeep, and any modifying or refitting, to achieve 1, 2, and 4, as well as day-to-day maintenance, all of which is economically tolerable. |
| 4 | Efficient use: | the use in terms of location, space provision and layout for logistical and ergonomical efficiency at tolerable levels. |

The serviceability states need to be considered for initial design and build.   Continuing satisfaction with built facilities with these states by the client is very much time dependant, hence time is a critical factor. Eventually a combination of considerations will result in an end of service life. How often do we as an industry receive feedback on how well this will concur with the designed service life - particularly on the safety critical structural integrity state?

Should we not try to develop systems which alert us to impending problems. Once built and commissioned a positive serviceability awareness monitoring programme would need to be implemented. To enable this to happen, however, a number of parameters need to be known, such as the loading conditions, materials used, build quality, condition and behaviour of the structure. Acquisition of knowledge is required for such an assessment to be made.

The awareness programme may need to be amended in the light of new knowledge to know whether a structure is acceptably within its structural serviceability state. The stimulus is often historical knowledge, in general, of the performance of other facilities. It might also be as a result of new research work or failures which have occurred to other facilities of either other similar structures or structures with similar features. The risk of catastrophic collapse of all or part of existing structures, or the potential for such an occurrence is thus substantially reduced.

Knowledge and prediction of behaviour of structures can be said to be based on historical knowledge which is modified by performance knowledge of other facilities, and failures. A critical factor, however, is the competence to be able to assess the significance of that data and make decisions about the future serviceable life. These skills can be brought together under an all embracing "forensic engineering" banner.

### WHAT SHOULD REASONABLY BE EXPECTED - by Clients?

What should clients reasonably expect. Their expectations should emerge after a thorough understanding of both what is realistically possible and also at what cost. The "realistically possible" tag comes with a heavy responsibility for engineers where their input is crucial to ensure that realistic expectations are deliverable. After an iterative process, the developed Client briefs should initiate a satisfactory job for all. Put simply, do owners know enough? There is an argument that the highly competitive market place, which now includes compulsory competitive tendering (CCT) and private finance initiatives (PFI) may not help in long term serviceability.

The Institution of Structural Engineers define structural engineering as:

> "The science and art of designing and making, with economy and elegance, buildings, bridges, frameworks, and other similar structures so that they can safely resist the forces to which they may be subjected."

The time seems to have come when that definition could be augmented by a phrase at the end of the statement for today's culture and market. At present it could be assumed that the missing word is "*inperpetuity*". The definition would then end "... ... so that they can safety resist the forces to which they may be subjected *inperpetuity*". Clearly this is not true and cannot be true, unless cost is not taken into account. For most reasonably practicable purposes the phrase to be added should arguably be "*for a specified life span*". The definition would then end "... ... so that they can safety resist the forces to which they may be subjected *for a specified life span*".

How easy is it to guarantee a specified life span?  This takes us back to the Clients expectations and to a clear Client brief.  An opportunity is created.  In retrospect, have we served, and are we still serving, our public well as an engineering profession?  The answer must be a resounding YES - especially in 1997, the year of YES - the "Year of Engineering Success".  This true to a very high confidence limit.  Why is this confidence limit not 100%.  The answer is of course because we continue to have serviceability failures.  Why is this?

## WHY IS THERE POOR SERVICEABILITY?

The fundamental reason is, arguably, education and knowledge, closely linked to application of that knowledge, together with any financial restraints.  Financial restraints may well not prove to provide the most economic solution in the medium or longer term, however.

Poor serviceability can result from criteria in the design, build, and/or operation of the facility and would be influenced by the investment in each.  Poor serviceability could, however, be attributed to lack of relevant competencies and the rigorous application of those competencies. Could this also apply to both professional  practitioners and academics?  Fewer incidents of poor serviceability should arise by improvements in a number of areas, including the following suggestions:

> Acquisition of appropriate knowledge;
> Application of appropriate knowledge;
> Realisation of limitations of knowledge;
> Retention of, and ability to retrieve, appropriate knowledge;
> Dissemination of appropriate knowledge, including any limitations;
> Dissemination of technical advances and innovations, together with any limitations, both known and unproven;
> Working more effectively within a competitive environment driven by "economy", including competition from other structural media;
> Monitoring of existing facilities to deal with changing conditions, including loadings;
> More rigorous assessment of designs or features before transferring the technology to other applications or environments;
> Effective use and maintenance strategies by owners and/or controllers of facilities.

Knowledge must of necessity be within the light of current knowledge.  More rigorous testing may be required in some instances before systems are brought into use.

The question needs to be asked Why are there sometimes inappropriate maintenance strategies?  Is it because owners have not been advised appropriately or at all.  Do owners know enough?   Why might they have they not developed and implemented appropriate regimes?

## LIKELIHOOD AND CONSEQUENCES OF FAILURE - THE RISKS

The **likelihood** of catastrophic failure is low.   The Standing Committee on Structural Safety (SCOSS) stated in their first Bulletin "Structural Safety 1994-96" [2], dated January 1997:

> "Over the past 2 years, the Standing Committee has observed a very good record, with a few exceptions, of structural safety in the United Kingdom.  World-wide there have been structural collapses and failures arising from extreme natural disasters on man-

made causes. These events provide a constant challenge for all who are concerned with structures of finding ways to avoid or minimise hazards to structures and to offset the risks. Acceptable standards in structural safety can only be achieved through the constant vigilance of engineers and others who have responsibility for safety".

The Bulletin summarised the recommendations and findings in the SCOSS Eleventh biannual report, published in January 1997 [3].

Although SCOSS are interested in many aspects of structural safety, which includes different structural materials and forms, their first three Immediate Priority Recommendations this year related to multi-storey car-parks. The first point dealt with inspection and appraisal [4] issues, which is an integral contributor to assessing serviceability of the structure, including prevention of structural failure. Since the SCOSS report was published there was a structural failure of a top slab in a reinforced concrete car park. It has been reported that amongst various criteria, poor concrete serviceability lead to catastrophic collapse of the structural slab.

The second Immediate Priority Recommendation dealt with adequacy of barriers. The example given was of a catastrophic failure of the vehicular restraint barrier system which included fixings to the concrete floor slab. A car fell from the forth floor concrete slab to the ground after the vehicular barrier system failed to restrain it. A number of issues were involved. The structure and fixings were approximately 20 years old. At the time of failure, the drill and fix bolt system was insufficient to resist the imposed forces, which might reasonably be expected, from vehicles. The design could easily have incorporated a safety back-up system, but didn't. The fixings were direct to the floor slab, where no upstand was provided. No advantage was taken of the columns.

The consequences of catastrophic failure can be considered in two principle areas, such as:

1)      health and safety of the public and of the workforce; and.
2)      financial.

Also the risk to workforce should be considered when they are required to maintain structures for long periods in potentially hazardous situations. There is thus a need to assess risks for structural safety [5], and also assessments for constructions [6].

The safety **consequences** of structural failure can vary, in terms of personal injury, from nil to fatal.     The risk of death from structural failure has been given as a probability of the 0.14 x $10^{-6}$ per person per calendar year [7]. Experience shows however that in the UK, and maybe else where, there a very high proportion of structural failures lead to nil personal injuries. It may be said that we are extremely lucky, but of course, there are still failures which cause fatalities. So the likelihood, even though low, of structural failure must be regarded as having high consequences.

The provisional figure by comparison, for occupational fatal injuries for in 1996/97 is about 300, giving an incident rate of 1.2 per 100,000 during the year. For construction fatalities, the figure is about 1/3rd at just under 100 people [8].

*Risk assessment example:* This example is based on work currently underway. The report summarises the results of a preliminary desk study and visual inspection of a bridge required for Phases 1 and 2 of a Special Inspection of the post-tensioned superstructure. It also includes a design review and risk appraisal of the substructure, in view of the suspected deterioration in the present condition of the pier wells.

A complete set of original design calculations, drawings and construction photographs provided the basis for the desk study. Further information was gathered from discussions with Engineers present at the time of construction and currently involved in monitoring the condition of the bridge. The study highlighted a series of important structural and material factors in both the original design assumptions and construction procedures, which would contribute to a significant loss of pre-compression in the concrete and subsequent changes in the fundamental behaviour of the superstructure.

The visual inspection confirmed the general external surfaces of the superstructure to be in good condition, in spite of a range of construction defects and structural cracking. The majority of the precast beams exhibited a variety of crack patterns, the most significant being a series of major flexural/shear cracks in the mid-span region. There was no direct evidence of internal corrosion of the pre-stressing tendons, but water was observed to be seeping from grout tubes located at mid-span in the bottom flanges and there were few signs of solid grout within the exposed vent tubes. Examination of the edge parapet details revealed the concrete parapet railings to carry very significant compressive forces, which reinforced the evidence relating to significant loss of pre-stress. Thus the parapet, footway and kerbs already appear to be making a significant contribution to the effective flexural stiffness of the edge beams.

Inspection of the deck and photographic evidence of the condition of the pier wells indicated significant deterioration in the substructure. At the expansion joints, direct contact exists between the adjacent decks on the downstream edge over pier 2. The closing of this gap implies that an in-plane rotational mechanism of the decks has occurred in response to an upstream deflection of the underlying pier well in an area where significant scour of the river bed has occurred. In addition, loss of brickwork from the tops of the pier wells carries with it the risk of rotation in the columns above or sudden shear failure of the remaining brickwork below.

The risk factors for this Viaduct have been identified from the desk study, preliminary inspection and photographic records. Separate risk assessments were undertaken for the critical deck spans and the worst known sections of the substructure. Although the design of the pier well foundations was found to be satisfactory, it is concluded there is a very high risk that any failure mechanism in the desk or pier wells would occur in a brittle manner. Hence, it is recommended that a regular monitoring regime be established as soon as possible, in order to detect any sudden deterioration in either the deck of the substructure.

It is concluded that the flexural shear cracking throughout the post-tensioned beams is due to an excessive loss of pre-stress, combined with extreme levels of live loading. Consequently, it is recommended that a load restriction of 20 tonne should be maintained and vehicle speeds reduced. Furthermore it is suggested that an intrusive examination of the grouting and tendons should be undertaken during Phrase 3 to assess the present condition of the cable wires and the long-term durability of the pre-stressing systems. Detailed material testing and concrete stress measurements are also suggested in order to explain the present condition of the critical beams in spans 13, 15, 21 and 22.

## THE WAY FORWARD

Some ways forward for enhancing long term serviceability of structures, including those of concrete, are suggested below, and principally based on the need for acquisition and dissemination of knowledge:

1. Creation of an international Significant EVent DAtaBase (SEVDAB) [9] to act a central depository for reported failures, from which trends can be seen. The information can be augmented and processed for development for promulgation to help prevent further such events.

2. Introduce positive serviceability awareness programmes. TO EXPAND!

3. Learning more from failures by developing the technology and methodology of investigations. This "forensic engineering" could be seen as a branch of engineering which relates to long term structure integrity serviceability, but can be applied on a far wider basis to other engineering disciplines. A Centre for Forensic Engineering, with these aims in mind and with both a British and an overseas perspective, is currently being developed at a UK University (in Cardiff).

4. Ensuring that professional "corporate" memory of failures endures so that those practising currently are aware of lessons learned in the past events. It is recognised that major failures tend to recur on an approximate 30 year cycle. A way to help with this is to introduce modules in undergraduate courses. A powerful way to help students understand the consequences of failure, both on a personal and professional level, is to include as an integral part of the module, a role-playing re-enactment case study of at least one such failure where there were authoritative inquiries. At least one UK university has introduced such a role-playing event. Such events could be set up as CPD for those who have recently qualified - and others.

5. The development of stability statements beyond erection processes to built facilities to record, following assessment, the identified structural integrity (both micro and macro) of a facility as an aid to ensuring that long term serviceability is maintained. Such statements can be used for the demolition and partial demolition process also. At least one UK university requires under graduates to produce stability statements in projects on erection of structures.

6. Educate client TO EXPAND!

## REFERENCES

1.    Latham M, *Constructing the team.* 1994. HMSO

2.    Standing Committee on Structural Safety. *SCOSS Bulletin Number 1, Structural Safety 1994-96.* 1997. Institution of Structural Engineers.

3.    Standing Committee on Structural Safety. *The Eleventh SCOSS Report, Structural Safety 1994-96: Review and recommendations.* 1997. Institution of Structural Engineers.

4.   Institution of Structural Engineers, *Appraisal of existing of structures.* Second Edition 1996. ISE.

5.   Menzies JB, Hazards, risks and structural safety. *The Structural Engineer Vol 73, No 21, 7 November 1995,* pp 357-63. Institution of Structural Engineers.

6.   Neale BS, Hazard and risk assessments for construction:   a regulators view. *The Structural Engineer, Vol.73, no.22, 21 November 1995,*   pp 388 - 90. Institution of Structural Engineers.

7.   Blockley D (Ed.), *Engineering Safety.* 1992. McGraw-Hill.

8.   Health and Safety Executive. *Safety Statistics Bulletin 1996/97. C40.* 1997. HSE.

9.   Neale BS. Designing for health and safety - the IT imperative. *Information Technology in Civil and Structural Engineering Design, pp81-5,* Civil-Comp Press, Edinburgh, 1996.

*Theme 1:*

**Design, Construction, Prediction and Inspection**

# Predicting and Achieving Serviceability

DR PAUL LAMBERT   PhD, CEng, MIM, FICorr
Associate, Mott MacDonald, Manchester, UK.

## SYNOPSIS
This paper outlines a personal view of the past, present and future of serviceable structures, with particular reference to the durability of reinforced concrete. Recent *bêtes noire* such as alkali aggregate reaction (AAR), are discussed along with some of the difficulties faced by the professional engineer when trying to successfully achieve the transition from specification to finished, durable structure.

A number of the options for improving the durability of reinforced concrete, and hence the serviceability of the resulting structures, are discussed. It is concluded that adequate serviceability is a product of careful control and supervision but also relies on the setting of realistic targets and the provision of adequate on-going maintenance.

Where standard concrete practice is unable to provide the required service life, the technology is available to increase durability by physical, chemical and electro-chemical means, albeit at additional cost.

## OBJECTIVES
The objectives of this paper are:

i)      to briefly consider the history of serviceable construction;

ii)     to discuss some recent problems associated with loss of serviceability;

iii)    to review new and developing technologies which promise to extent the service lives of reinforced concrete structures.

## INTRODUCTION
The civil and structural professions have a long and honourable history in which they can rightly take pride and from which have developed well-considered and carefully established procedures for the design and construction of safe, economic structures. Representing, as I do, the relatively young profession of materials and corrosion engineering, it would be all too  easy to be cynical about some of the mistakes that are made with regard to durability. The truth is, as more and more is demanded in terms of service-life, low maintenance and optimum use of expensive materials, the advantages of these and other disciplines working hand-in-hand becomes hard to ignore or resist.  This paper is a personal view of just what is possible, good and bad, and what must be achieved in the coming years when the term 'expensive' may refer as much to ecological matters as to economic ones.

*Management of concrete structures for long-term serviceability*. Thomas Telford, London, 1997

Overall, it is not a pessimistic view, particularly with regards to the various bodies represented at this seminar. Let us start at a time long before Telford (the great civil engineer, not the New Town), and see where it takes us.

## A BRIEF HISTORY OF TIME-TO-FIRST-MAINTENANCE

Our expectations of what a structure should be capable of achieving in terms of low-maintenance service-life are subject to the same cyclical swings of all things human. The Ancient Egyptians built their temples and burial chambers for a life eternal and all but managed it. Sadly, their modern-day counterparts fell into the western trap of good-enough-will-do. So while there are 2000+ year old structures designed for the single one-way journey of a departed pharaoh (or return journey, depending on one's faith), modern structures intended to serve many thousands of people for tens of years are unfit for use in periods better measured by months than millennia [1].

We in the west have our own examples. Why do English country villages almost inevitably sport impressive ancient churches and public houses dating back to the 16th century and beyond? Where are the 'ordinary' buildings, where the common folk lived and worked? They are not there. The church and pub were well conceived, well built and well maintained. The farm labourers' homes were thrown-up using cheap materials, unskilled labour and left to rot using a sort of medieval system-built approach with low-rise wattle and daub rather than high-rise concrete and misery.

## THOROUGHLY MODERN MATERIALS

We know so much more now about the nature of structural materials. The work carried out on steel reinforced concrete over, say, the last twenty years is awesome. Since the early seventies we now know, in detail, how the various Portland cement minerals hydrate and their relative importance within the complex matrix that is cement paste. We understand the protective mechanism of concrete on embedded steel - way beyond the simplistic concepts of barrier and buffer [2].

We have re-discovered pozzolanic materials and analysed their behaviour. Cement replacements such as pulverised fuel ash, blast furnace slag and micro-silica are now relatively commonplaces, salving both the economic and ecological consciences as they are all otherwise waste products demanding costly storage and disposal. In a twist of irony, there is even talk of producing blast furnace slag as a primary product, with the pig iron being, at least in principal, 'waste'.

Even in relatively recent times there have been 'new' evils to face. Alkali aggregate reaction has kept concrete technologists and the media busy for a number of years. Now we understand why and how this often over-hyped problem occurs it should be no more onerous to avoid than sulphate attack. AAR is, of course, as old as the hills and research was carried out in the UK during the 1930's and 40's on behalf of our colonial cousins. We just forgot about it [3].

As an aside, during the peak of the AAR furore, the laboratory I was working in as a research assistant was contacted by the BBC in the hope that we could provide some 'reactive aggregate' to show on a popular science programme. They also asked if they could have their presenter pour some alkali onto this material, presumably to see it fizz and bubble.

Despite the offer of a motorcycle dispatch rider to collect the material, the request was declined. The programme went ahead unabated with the eager public dutifully shown what looked suspiciously like a mixture of sand and baking powder onto which was dribbled, to great effect, what one can only assume was vinegar.

Given the (continuing) track record of the programme in question, it is perhaps a shame that we did not try harder to properly demonstrate AAR, as it would then have almost certainly never been heard of again. Instead, of course, we now had a miss-informed public who could visualise their home dissolving in a cloud of froth. Most helpful.

Elsewhere, when the media and popular press have strayed from the factual to the fanciful (and let's face it, they prefer a tangent to a straight line every time), there have been occasions where the tenants in entire blocks of flats have voiced their concerns over the 'concrete cancer' associated with their building, and whether or not they could catch it.

## TOMORROW'S WORLD
Back in the laboratory, much has already been done to understand the physics, mechanics, chemistry and electrochemistry of structural materials. We already know sufficient to define how one can achieve optimum durability in most common environments. It is vital work, and it can only be effectively carried out by competent academics operating within well organised and hopefully adequately funded research facilities.

What it generally tells us about structural materials is good - it will last a long time and can survive incredibly aggressive environments. But we must be cautious about how we apply this information or we will be badly tripped-up. Such work is essential to define the absolute limits of the performance envelope into which all structural materials must reside. It does not always tell us what to expect in real life.

Taking the example of reinforced concrete, for which I make no apologies for being most familiar with, there is a universe of difference between the small specimens crafted in the laboratory and the massive structures they try to model. For a start, 50 kg of concrete prepared by a post-doc, two research students and a technician is not the same as 200 m$^3$ poured on site. The well-trodden lab-crete/real-crete argument. But it goes much further than this old chestnut.

Concrete is specified and judged *on average* but generally fails *in particular*. This is very much the case with regard to corrosion-related problems associated with the reinforcement. Corrosion problems are typically the result of either loss of alkalinity due to carbonation of the cover or the ingress of significant levels of chloride ions from some external source (ignoring internal sources of chloride ion for the time being). Factors such as low cover, locally misplaced steel, honeycombing and cracking can all have a profound effect on how long the reinforcement can resist the urge to return to its oxide roots. In general, structures do not exhibit reduced serviceability due to the average or typical characteristics but as a consequence of their local deficiencies and defects. The more that can be done to prevent or limit such local effects must have a profound influence on the durability and hence serviceability of any structure. It is worth remembering that the only time reinforcement is in precisely the correct position is usually on the drawings [4].

## CP OR NOT CP

Some of the most interesting and innovative approaches to increasing the durability of structural materials, again inevitably concentrating on reinforced concrete, are associated with the repair of existing structures [5]. In a surprisingly short time-scale, techniques such as cathodic protection (CP), re-alkalisation, chloride extraction and corrosion inhibition have become quite widely accepted and increasingly applied. Cathodic protection and the application of corrosion inhibitors have both been comprehensively employed by other industries over a considerable period of time.

Cathodic protection dates back to the golden age of British technical innovation, with none other than Humphrey Davy coming up with a solution to the rotting iron nails used to secure the copper bottom to HMS Alarm. Since that time, the aim has generally been to use cathodic protection from new to prevent or limit the problem of corrosion in the first place. One would not expect the owners of pipelines, oilrigs and ships to wait for them to leak or sink (as appropriate), prior to applying the protection. We still do with this with reinforced concrete bridges, tunnels, car parks and the like. But technically we do not need to. In fact, from a technical basis it is significantly easier (and therefore cheaper), to apply cathodic protection to a reinforced concrete structure from new. It has been done, but not often, nor will it be as long as *price-now* dominates *cost-eventually*.

There is a much better track record for corrosion inhibitors being used from new in concrete structures, but the recent revival of interest in the technology rests largely with materials suitable for use in repair. As inhibitors are often specified for use in parallel with some form of corrosion monitoring, this is also proving to be an effective way of getting structures instrumented and monitored over significant proportions of their service-lives.

## THE SHAPE OF THINGS TO COME

There are a number of other factors relating to the serviceability of new structures initially identified by R&D but subsequently rejected by D&B. Alternatives to conventional carbon steel reinforcement seem to have much less of an impact than one might expect and yet epoxy coated or stainless steel reinforcement have much to offer if used appropriately. Coatings to concrete, whether to prevent the ingress of carbon dioxide, chlorides or moisture are exceedingly hard to specify from new but ubiquitous on repaired structures. For some reason I have yet to understand, there is a general dislike of painted concrete (surely no one still thinks it looks like Portland stone), while bare steel is an anathema hence, presumably, the poor showing of weathering steels.

So how are we to determine what is and is not a good idea for our new structures to ensure that they outlast those who designed and built them rather than just their warranty periods? How are we to best use expensive resources that consume large amounts of energy in a world where ecological considerations, both real and contrived for reasons of convenience, are given increasing priority? We have already progressed from NIMBY (not in my back yard) to BANANA (build absolutely nothing anywhere near anyone). Presumably soon it will be 'ask Sir Swampy whether it's permissible ever'. I wouldn't recommend trying that one.

Instead let us consider in greater detail some of the options available for employing resources more effectively through enhancing the durability of reinforced concrete and thereby achieving the serviceability demanded:

## Design And Specification For Durability

The design and specification of most structural concrete is carried out in accordance with codified recommendations based largely on past experience and accepted good practice at the time of writing.

Documents generally evolve slowly over a number of years, incorporating only minor modifications and amendments. New and innovative techniques and materials can only therefore be incorporated after relatively lengthy periods and as experience of their successful application increases. These points can be illustrated by reference to the relevant British Standards but are true for most codified methods of guidance.

In the UK, standards such as BS8110:1985 detail the requirements for a durable concrete mix design primarily in terms of strength and largely ignores many other properties which influence durability. Water/cement (w-c) ratio, minimum cement content and depth of cover to reinforcement are defined for concrete in relation to various grades of environmental exposure from mild to extreme. The inability of this system to always work satisfactorily, particularly in the more severe environments, is demonstrated by the number of structures that fail within their design life.

Fundamental questions concerning rates of deterioration in a given environment, such as the rate of penetration of aggressive species, cannot be predicted using these methods. It is therefore not possible to reliably estimate the duration of each of the stages of deterioration and hence obtain the likely maintenance-free life of the structure.

The properties of individual components are often covered by their own standards which are occasionally in conflict with the specification for concrete. For example, in the UK, BS12 : Ordinary Portland Cement (OPC) allows it to contain up to 0.1% $Cl^-$, while BS8110 states that for pre-stressed concrete the maximum allowable $Cl^-$ concentration (by weight of cement) is also 0.1%. Therefore if the cement used in the manufacture of a pre-stressed unit is OPC and it contains its maximum allowable level of $Cl^-$ then no chloride ions are permitted to be incorporated from any other source. This makes compliance with the specification difficult, if not impossible, to achieve.

The use of inappropriate standards for the design of structures has also lead to problems of concrete durability. In the UK, the use of BS8007 to limit crack widths in structures designed to retain aqueous liquids has frequently been specified for the design of structures which retain aggressive liquids, such as in the handling and treatment of chemical effluent. This is despite the fact that the introduction to this standard clearly states that it is not applicable for aggressive fluids.

Although there are clearly problems associated with the use of codes and standards, this approach works reasonably well for every-day, ordinary, non-aggressive environments. Where structures of major importance are to be exposed to severe environments a different approach must be adopted, based on the classification of the environment and the fundamental properties of the structural materials [6].

## Characterisation of the Service Environment

In the UK, British Standards classify the service environment of the concrete into five groups, based on exposure to moisture, chloride and frost action. However, none of these parameters is quantified in terms of concentration or number of cycles of action, etc. Quantification of environmental parameters is essential if durability design is to be successfully performed.

The classification of environments by the BRE for acid and sulphate attack goes part of the way along this route, in that five classes and two sub-classes are defined with relation to the concentrations of aggressive ions present in the soil or groundwater [7]. This type of approach can be followed to classify environments for other potential mechanisms of deterioration.

Rigorous site investigation must be undertaken to collect the necessary basic data on:

- ionic concentrations in the ground, groundwater and atmosphere,
- pH of groundwater and any rate of flow data,
- temperature variation,
- relative humidity variation,
- rainfall pattern and frequency,
- organic compounds.

The orientation of a particular structure on a site and the influence of design in the inadvertent formation of corrosive micro-environments where, for example, high concentrations of aggressive ions accumulate, may be important. The internal environment likely to occur within the structure when it is in service also has an effect on the durability of the concrete.

For example, the concrete lining of a tunnel may be cool and water saturated at the extrados and hot and dry ($40°C$, 25% RH) at the intrados. The concrete will need to be designed to accommodate both of these environments. The behaviour of concrete in structures in similar environments to those expected (particularly the internal environment) should be examined to obtain basic performance data.

## Options for Improving Durability

The durability performance of new reinforced concrete structures can be greatly enhanced by the adoption of one or several options, most of which have already been referred to. Many are also relevant for the repair and refurbishment of existing structures. All of the following approaches have been applied to recently constructed or refurbished structures.

### *Enhanced Quality Concrete*

The requirements for the specification and production of high quality concrete suitable for the construction of durable reinforced concrete structures are well identified in relevant codes and standards.

One area of potential improvement that has been successfully employed on many recent major construction programmes is the use of cement replacement materials such as ground granulated blast furnace slag (GGBS), and pulverised fuel ash (PFA). When used in low water-cement ratio mixes, these materials can help to produce concrete with low permeability and high resistance to ionic diffusion.

The performance of concrete can potentially be further enhanced by the judicious addition of special concrete admixtures, for example, permeability reducers such as ammonium stearate.

## Protective Coatings

Coatings can be used to protect concrete substrates in a number of ways. They can form an impermeable barrier between the environment and the substrate and in this way afford almost complete protection, assuming the coating is continuous. Coatings can also protect the substrate by slowing down the rate of penetration of aggressive components from the environment into the substrate, ie. they provide partial protection, which may be adequate to allow the structure to fulfil its design life.

There are at present a large number of mainly organic coatings available to protect structural materials such as reinforced concrete from many different service environments. In addition to epoxies, polyurethanes and bituminous systems there is now an increasing use of penetrating water repellent pore liners. Water repellents in current use are generally based on silanes and siloxanes and guidelines have been produced for their application to UK highway structures.

## Epoxy Coated Reinforcement

Fusion bonded epoxy coated reinforcement (FBECR), is produced under carefully controlled factory conditions. The majority of FBECR is coated by electrostatic spraying onto straight bars which are subsequently bent and cut. For the production of tunnel segment reinforcement cages, particular success has been achieved by coating the prefabricated cages by means of fluidised bed dipping to give a thicker coating with fewer defects, particularly at joints and bends.

The presence of a thin, coherent and relatively defect free epoxy layer helps isolate the steel from potentially aggressive species in the concrete, notably chloride ions. Even where the coating contains small defects, the large distances between adjacent defects helps limit the magnitude of corrosion currents that can flow. With all epoxy coated reinforcement there is some reduction in pull-out resistance, increase in crack widths and greater deflections which must be taken into account during the design phase.

## Cathodic Protection

Cathodic protection is a means of protecting steel from aggressive chloride-laden environments. The steel is maintained as the cathode in an electrical circuit driven by either an impressed current or, less commonly for reinforced concrete, a sacrificial anode.

Cathodic protection systems must be carefully designed and account must be taken of many different factors such as the aggressiveness of the environment; the area of steel to be protected; the resistivity of the surrounding material; the positioning of any external metallic objects which could be affected by the system; the type of anode used etc.

The initial design requirements and the application of a current throughout the service life of the structure being protected can make cathodic protection expensive and complex in comparison to conventional repair systems. A careful evaluation of cathodic protection systems relative to other repair options should be made in order to ascertain whether cathodic protection is the best route to follow.

In addition to using cathodic protection as part of a repair strategy for corrosion damaged concrete, the technique is also being developed for the protection of new structures, including post-tensioned members. Because passive steel requires less polarisation to achieve protection, stressed tendons can be included without the usual concerns of hydrogen embrittlement.

Continuing developments in the method of application and available anode systems, such as sprayed conductive overlays, promise to extend the use of this technique in both new and existing structures.

### Corrosion Inhibitors for Reinforced Concrete

Corrosion inhibitors are widely used in the protection of metals. There has long been interest in their potential use for the protection of concrete reinforcement, generally as admixtures of calcium nitrite. A more recent development has been in the availability of inhibitor systems that can be applied to the surface of reinforced concrete or injected into the body of the concrete and then migrate to and protect the steel.

It is apparent from the work carried out to date that corrosion inhibitor systems applied topically or as a concrete admixture have the potential to significantly reduce the rate of chloride induced corrosion in structures. With increasing availability of such materials it is hoped that further independent research and trials will be initiated to prove their performance and effectiveness in comparison with other remedial techniques for corrosion control.

There is particular interest in their use with pre-stressed and other AAR-susceptible structures where the use of cathodic protection may be undesirable [8].

## CONCLUSIONS

Optimising serviceability is clearly possible provided realistic targets are initially set and all subsequent activities are subject to rigorous control and supervision. We are in possession of sufficient background information and practical experience to be able to perform the diagnoses of what is and prognoses of what will be.

Concrete no longer needs to be a vague grey bulk, specified only by strength. Like steel, it's properties can be defined to a considerable degree of subtlety. Unlike steel, it is not generally manufactured under factory conditions and therefore demands a much greater degree of experienced supervision, particularly during placing and curing. Where we now know that even the best concrete is not enough, we are able to further enhance performance with physical barriers, chemical additives and electro-chemical enhancements.

Good design and competent site practice are within the control of the professional engineer and contractor. The third factor, adequate maintenance throughout the life of the structure, is more likely to be the concern of the owner. It is therefore the responsibility of the engineers and contractors to demonstrate the commercial advantages that can be gained from the establishment of a properly conceived and effectively performed maintenance programme.

## REFERENCES

1. Wood, J G M. Henderson Colloquium on Design Life of Structures, IABSE - British Group, Pembroke College, Cambridge, 1990.

2. Page, C L and Treadaway, K W J. Aspects of the Electrochemistry of Steel in Concrete, Nature, Vol.297, No.5862, May 1982, pp 109-115.

3. Alkali-Silica Reaction - Minimising the Risk of Damage to Concrete, Technical Report No.30, The Concrete Society, 1987.

4. Lambert, P. Corrosion and Protection of Reinforced Concrete - An Overview, Corrosion & Protection of Reinforced Concrete, ICorr/Concrete Society, Dubai,1994, 16pp.

5. Lambert, P. Reinforced Concrete Repair Reviewed, Highways, October 1996, pp 14-16.

6. Leek, D S, Lambert, P, Harper, A M and Ecob, C R. The Specification and Production of High Quality Reinforced Concrete for Durability, International Conference on Corrosion Protection of Steel in Concrete, University of Sheffield, 1994, 11pp.

7. Sulphate (sic) and Acid Resistance of Concrete in the Ground, BRE, Digest 363, 1996.

8. Lambert, P. Overview of Electrochemical Protection and the Future Positioning of Corrosion Inhibitors, International Conference on Corrosion Inhibitor Technology in Concrete, Flims, Switzerland, September 1996, 16pp.

# Service Life Design of Concrete Structures - Current and Emerging Approaches

BOB CATHER AND DR BRYAN MARSH  PhD, CEng, MICE, MICT, FCS
Ove Arup & Partners, London, England

## SYNOPSIS

Design of concrete structures for a specific life is becoming increasingly necessary, particularly where the required service life is significantly greater than normal, where the exposure conditions are particularly aggressive, or where there is a lower than normal acceptable risk of failure. Nevertheless, current UK standards and codes of practice give little assistance in designing for a specific life. Indeed, most design guidance gives little indication even of what life can be expected when a structure is designed and constructed according to that guidance. The situation is much the same in most other countries. The advent of Eurocodes for design of structures will, however, introduce service life design as a specific consideration and the supporting standards will contain durability guidance related to classes of required service life.

Service life design is particularly relevant to concrete structures as most of the principal deterioration mechanisms that affect them, such as carbonation-induced and chloride-induced corrosion of reinforcement, are time dependant.

This paper discusses the need for service life design for concrete structures and considers some possible approaches. It briefly reviews the current state of the art, including limitations of the approach, and identifies areas where further work is required.

## OBJECTIVES

The intention of this paper is to:

- Outline the need for service life design of concrete structures
- Review the available guidance in current British Standards
- Predict the impact of forthcoming European Standards
- Outline the current state-of-art and identify its limitations and the need for further work

*Management of concrete structures for long-term serviceability.* Thomas Telford, London, 1997

## SERVICE LIFE DESIGN

It is perhaps necessary at the onset of this paper to make clear what is meant by service life design. It is the process of designing a structure or element to meet a client's requirement for a specific minimum period of time during which no excessive unplanned expenditure is required on operation, maintenance or repair.

The actual service life of a structure, or 'working life' as it is known in European Standards and EC directives, can be conveniently split into three types (Beeby, 1993):

technical service life:
> time in service until a defined unacceptable state is reached

functional service life:
> time in service until the structure becomes obsolete due to change in functional requirements

economic service life:
> time in service until replacement of the structure is economically more advantageous than keeping the structure in service

Any one of these can actually determine the actual end of use. Economic service life and functional service life are, however, generally beyond the control of the original designer so this paper is primarily concerned with 'technical service life'. It has been suggested (Beeby, 1993) that technical and functional service life are contained within the definition of economic service life because many shortcomings can be overcome by repair or refurbishment, and this will be controlled by economics. Probably the only exception is sudden collapse. The end of life is thus, in his opinion, when it is no longer economical to keep the structure or component 'alive'. Even this, however, may not be a suitable definition in the case of an historical monument where economic arguments may be overridden by other reasons for keeping it 'in service'. Whether or not these arguments are accepted, technical service life is probably the only one that can form the basis of a rational durability design.

## THE NEED FOR SERVICE LIFE DESIGN

Many of the deterioration mechanisms affecting structures in general, and concrete structures in particular, are time-related. Specific examples for concrete structures include the corrosion of reinforcement induced by carbonation or ingress of chlorides. It therefore seems logical to include time as a major parameter in the design process. As will be seen later, this is not generally the case. Indeed, how many people consider service life design when buying their own house? There appears to be an inherent, unquestioned belief that it is not a problem. Admittedly there may be a general realisation that parts of the building have a finite life, such as windows and roof tiles, but not this is not extended to the building as a whole. Perhaps even more disturbing is the surprisingly common view that reinforced concrete is a maintenance free product that lasts for ever.

The layman may be excused for not considering lifetime but not so the specialist. Indeed, the understanding of the degradation factors and resultant deterioration mechanisms in concrete has grown steadily through at least eight decades of research. The result has been a much more sophisticated product than the simple combination of cement, water, sand and gravel that was once concrete. An increasing range of binders, aggregates, coatings and admixtures, and innovations such as permeable formwork and cathodic protection, mean concrete can now be equipped to meet the increasing demands being made of it. One such demand is the requirement from informed clients for structures that can be assured to perform for a certain lifetime without the need for anything more than scheduled maintenance. A particular service life requirement is being increasingly specified. Examples include a commercial office building in London (50 years for the structure, 25 years for cladding, less for services), new offices for Government in London (125 years), the new British Library (an assumed 'extended life' of, say, 500 years) and some proposed storage structures which have a required service life of no less than $10^5$ years!

The established design approach, which uses values of cover to reinforcement, minimum strength grade, minimum cement content and maximum water/cement ratio, etc., that are prescribed in standards and codes of practice, is probably fine for 'normal' or short required service lives. There is inevitably a mismatch between the recommendations in standards and reality but this may be small within this timescale, although there are doubts about the success of the established approach under some exposure conditions. Under a longer timescale this mismatch can become significant and any shortfall in requirements can result in unsatisfactory performance in service. A more considered approach is required where the required service life is significantly longer than 'normal', where the exposure conditions are particularly aggressive, or where there is a lower than normal acceptable risk of failure of the structure to perform as required. These conditions may appear undesirably vague but it is difficult, at the current stage of development, to say exactly when the required service life is sufficiently long, or what exposure conditions are suitably aggressive, etc.. Until more detailed guidance is available, probably necessitating a greater understanding of the applicability of current code recommendations, the designer's decision of when to go for a service life design approach must remain purely subjective.

A further reason for the development of service life design is the need to unravel the complex relationship between materials, design and construction which governs durability in practice (O'Brien, Cather and Figg, 1987). This is not considered explicitly in the established prescriptive approach whereby general guidance is given and it is then assumed that all is well and good. Some major infrastructure projects, such as the Jubilee Line Extension have moved some way down this road through the use of performance specification instead of conventional prescriptive requirements alone. Performance specification have the potential to be tailored to ensure the concrete will have the required properties, in the structure, to resist the encountered degradation factors for the required service life.

## END OF SERVICE LIFE

The definition of technical service life at the beginning of the paper begs the question of what should be the 'defined unacceptable state' that marks the end of the life. Attempting an answer to that question could, however, form the basis of an entire paper in its own right. The Holmes' concept for the Deacon's one-hoss shay 'that was built in such a logical way, it ran for one hundred years to a day' and then 'went to pieces all at once, all at once and nothing first, just as bubbles do when they burst' would probably not be acceptable to the owners of most concrete structures. Indeed, even if desirable, such precision is not possible considering all the variable influences on a concrete structure.

The occurrence of spalling is considered by Beeby (1993) to be beyond the end of service life as it reflects a reduction in safety of the structure and of any passers-by who could be struck by falling spalled concrete. A reasonable limit for reinforcement corrosion might be taken as that resulting in surface crack widths of 0.3mm, which is a limit commonly considered for structural cracks. Alternatively, there is the view that no corrosion should be allowed during the design life. This brings problems, where the end point is defined as when corrosion initiation occurs but the conditions for significant propagation do not exist. Examples are indoor concrete or concrete permanently submerged under sea water. There are also problems with the definition, for example, of the carbonation front. Scatter can be very large and it can be shown that the 'life' based on a mean carbonation front can be up to three times as great as the life based on a characteristic front.

Selection of a criterion for the end of service life as strict as a maximum crack width is probably inappropriate at this stage in the development of service life design as there are no reliable methods available to relate crack width due to corrosion of reinforcement to time. The designer is thus forced to make a broad assumption about the time from initiation of corrosion to corrosion-induced cracking resulting in the pre-determined unacceptable state.

A further complication is added where the end point is redefined and the required service life becomes a moving target. This can happen even where designers and clients originally had a reasonably clear understanding of the concept of, or need for, service life design. There are numerous examples, including postwar prefabricated housing, offshore oil platforms and nuclear power stations, where the required life has changed significantly during use. Such changes may be the result of factors such as market influences, economics or changes in technology. There is also the increasing awareness of environmental issues whereby re-use is seen as preferable to recycling. Guidance is clearly needed, for clients and designers alike, on the definition of the unacceptable state and what life to specify before that state may be reached.

## CURRENT UK AND OTHER NATIONAL STANDARDS
Standards and Codes of Practice in the UK generally represent the collective agreement of an acceptable level of good practice. In some areas this is becoming less the case, with a predominance of specialists being involved in new drafting. This can result in standards that are more the result of 'current thinking' and research findings. A result of this tendency is an increased rate of change in recommendations and guidance that may mean many typical 'front line' designers may get left behind.

The concept of design life, or required service life, is not specifically covered in most current British Standards for concrete structures. This situation is known to be true also of most of the rest of Europe (Marsh, 1993) and is believed to be true virtually world-wide. There are, however, a few notable exceptions to this:

The handbook to the 1985 version of BS8110 (1985), for the design of concrete structures, contains the following statements:
> 'The intended life of the structure must, obviously, be considered at the outset together with the defined, or likely, maintenance.
>
> As with other structural materials, knowledge is not yet adequate to allow concrete structures to be designed for a specific durability and life. Structures designed and built according to the recommendations in the Code may normally be expected to be sufficiently resistant to the aggressive effects of the environment that maintenance and repair of the concrete will not be required for several decades; i.e. a life before significant maintenance generally in the region of say 50-100 years.'

There is, however, no mention of design life or service life in the standard itself or indeed in the 1997 revision (BS 8110 : Part 1, 1997). This might be considered to be a sad reflection on our research and knowledge base if the statement about our inadequate knowledge can be believed to be true after more than a hundred years experience of reinforced concrete construction and almost as many years of research. Revolution (or evolution) would appear to be long overdue.

Other UK codes which, at first view, appear to have moved forward on design life are, in practice, no better. For example, the current British Standard Code of Practice for maritime structures (BS 6349, 1984) contains guidance on values of minimum design life for different types of structure, ranging from 30 years for superstructure works to 100 years for flood protection works. The detailed durability guidance is, however, not directly related to these values of design life and there is no specific guidance on the factors that control this.

The draft revision of this code (BSI, 1997) has addressed the issue of design life in more detail with the following statements:
> 'The durability of concrete in maritime conditions is dependent upon the recognition of environmental exposure conditions and the adoption of appropriate design, detailing, materials and workmanship to suit those conditions.
>
> These factors may be forecast, which together with careful design, detailing, choice of materials and construction techniques can result in a design working life of at least 50 years for reinforced concrete.
>
> Plain concrete, subject to the same provisos, has a design working life of at least 100 years.'

More significantly, the durability guidance now contains mix design limits specifically for 50 years for reinforced and 100 years for plain concrete. Nevertheless, examination of the values for maximum water/cement ratio and minimum cement content reveals that they are clearly based on the values in the current edition for which no design life is indicated. They are, therefore, probably more a case of service life prediction than service life design! Moreover, the designer is presented with no information on measures necessary to extend the design life for reinforced concrete to, say, 100 years. The rather vague statement about '*appropriate* design, detailing, materials and workmanship' is of little practical use. A case of providing every assistance short of actual help? There is thus considerable scope for improvement in our standards. Indeed, one of the few standards containing specific design life information, for agricultural buildings and structures (BS5502), actually had this removed at its last revision!

## FORTHCOMING EUROPEAN AND INTERNATIONAL STANDARDS
The advent of European Standardization is already having a significant impact on thinking on service life design, and this before a single full standard relating to concrete structures has been published! This stems from the specific mention of life in the following requirement in the prestandard Eurocode 1 for the basis of design (ENV 1991-1, 1994):

'A structure shall be designed and executed in such a way that it will, *during its intended life*...
- remain fit for the use for which it is required; and
- sustain all actions and influences likely to occur during execution and use.'

In itself, this is little different from the stated aim of design in BS8110 (1997) which also refers to the 'intended life':

> 'The aim of design is the achievement of an acceptable probability that structures being designed will perform satisfactorily *during their intended life*. With an appropriate degree of safety, they should sustain all the loads and deformations of normal construction and use and have adequate durability...'

Where the European prestandard takes a significant step ahead of BS8110, and most other similar documents around the world, is by the quantification of the intended working life in terms of a 'required design working life', the classes of which are reproduced below in table 1:

Table 1:      Indicated values of required design working life from ENV 1991-1 (1994)

| Class | Required design working life (years) | Examples |
|-------|-------------------------------------|----------|
| 1 | [1-5] | Temporary structures |
| 2 | [25] | Replaceable structural parts, e.g. gantry girders, bearings |
| 3 | [50] | Building structures and other common structures |
| 4 | [100] | Monumental building structures, bridges, and other civil engineering structures |

The numbers in the table are referred to only as 'indicated values'. Indeed, they are given as 'boxed values' which means that alternative values can be used on a national basis. Despite this somewhat timid introduction of service life design, the draft European Standard for concrete (prEN206, 1997) has adopted the classification and developed the concept further by inclusion of durability provisions for an intended life of at least 50 years. Unfortunately this classification system is not unique and at least two rival versions appear in other key documents including BS7543 (1992) and the draft ISO standard for service life design of buildings (ISO, 1995). The ISO document uses a design life classification based on that in the Japanese service life design guide (AIJ, 1993), ie 150 years (DL150), 100 years (DL100), 60 years (DL60), 40 years (DL40), 25 years (DL25), 15 years (DL15), and up to 10 years (DL10). It will, however, be up to the client, or to the designer in consultation with the client, to decide which category the structure will lie. In common with the house buyers mentioned earlier, many clients will have little idea of the concept of required service life and will require guidance, often from the designer himself.

Informative Annex H of prEN206 contains guidance on 'alternative performance-related design methods with respect to durability'. It is intended to prepare the way for the use of such techniques, as an alternative to the standard method of design based on tables of limiting values of parameters such as minimum strength grade and maximum water/cement ratio for a given minimum life under certain exposure conditions. The alternative methods that are mentioned are:

- The refinement of the standard method, based on long-term experience of local materials and practices, and on detailed knowledge of the local environment.
- Methods based on approved and proven tests which are representative of actual conditions and have approved performance criteria.

- Methods based on analytical models, which have been calibrated against test data representative of actual conditions in practice.

The draft standard says the alternative approach may be appropriate where:
- a working life outside the normal range of 50-75 years is required
- the structure is 'special' requiring a lower probability of failure
- the environmental actions are particularly aggressive, or are well defined
- standards of workmanship are expected to be high
- a management and maintenance strategy is to be introduced, perhaps with planned upgrading
- significant populations of similar structures, or elements, are to be built
- new or different materials are to be used
- re-analysis of cases where the standard method has been used in design, but there has been a compliance failure

The validity of some of these statements might be questionable but the annex seems to have its heart in the right place.

The development of the draft complementary UK concrete standard to EN206 has gone one step ahead of EN206 itself and considers intended working lives of at least 50 years and at least 100 years. This was in response to the belief that 50 years was inadequate for many civil engineering structures including bridges. The BSI Working Group was thus provided with a real challenge. Two different service lives meant it could not take the easy route, as done in the draft revision to the maritime structures code, by using the values from, say, BS8110 and declaring them to be suitable for a 50 year life. Provisional values are included in the BSI Draft for Public Comment of prEN206 (prEN206, 1997). These are the result of a fundamental review of the guidance in existing British Standard Codes of Practice including BS 8110 (1997), BS 6349 (1984) and BS 5400 (1990). The review considered current practice, past performance and published research data applicable specifically to UK conditions. The Working Group examined each of the major deterioration mechanisms of concrete and reinforcement and attempted to determine how these are quantitatively dependent upon the principle specification parameters (cement type, concrete grade, cement content, water/cement ratio and air content). A lack of data for some conditions, severe constraint on the available time, and differences in technical opinion between experts meant that many of the values are the result of compromise and informed judgment.

Both authors of this paper have been, and continue to be, intimately involved in the development of this guidance and can safely say it has been an enlightening experience, to say the least! It was an unpleasant surprise to discover quite how much research data cannot readily be translated into practical guidance and to discover significant areas where almost no useful information was available. An example of this is the time from the onset of corrosion of reinforcement to the point when surface cracking is clearly visible; the point at that might have been chosen to define the end of the service life. This adds to the already extensive uncertainty that exists due to the lack of accuracy involved in prediction of the rate of ingress of chlorides and the level necessary at the reinforcement for initiation of corrosion. Admittedly, numerical models are available but not yet, it would seem, with satisfactory practical validation.

The draft European Standards seem to have set the service life design ball rolling. The worry is that it is rolling down hill and the available design guidance may not yet be able to run fast enough to trap it.

## SOME UNHELPFUL CURRENT GUIDANCE

Much well intentioned guidance in various documents unfortunately turns out in practice to be almost useless. As an example, the draft European Standard for concrete, prEN206, contains a particularly unhelpful note relating to design working lives other than the 50 years assumed in that standard:

> 'For shorter or longer working life, less onerous or more severe limiting values may be required. In these cases...special considerations have to be made by the specifier for a specific site or by national provisions in general'

The same is true of the Handbook to BS8110 which glibly states:

> 'It is for the client, designer, specifier, manufacturer or contractor as appropriate, to make the choices necessary for the construction of a specific structure. These choices should be made following consideration of the uncertainties which are likely to be present in particular aspects of the design and construction phases and also of the subsequent use and environment of the structure in service. Where a greater uncertainty than usual is judged to be present in a particular aspect it should be offset by adopting a more cautious, or stringent, approach or by introducing alternative safeguards.
>
> Where a higher than usual degree of assurance of durability is required, choices should be made which ensure that the structure and its maintenance will be of higher than usual quality.'

Will no-one come to the aid of the poor designer?

## CURRENT PERCEPTIONS OF DESIGN LIFE

A common value for design life of a building in the back of the mind of the designer is likely to be 60 years. This value does not appear in codes but probably has its routes in the payback period for local authority financed housing. A value of 80 years was encountered recently by one the authors for a school refurbishment which, it is believed, reflected the payback period in Scotland for a proposed new wing. The value of 120 years for highway bridges (BS5400:Part 4, 1990) is more traceable although it is believed to be based on estimates of the time to finance complete replacement of country's bridge stock. It would be interesting to derive a new design life requirement for bridges based on replacement of the whole UK bridge stock at current levels of financing! It is worthy of note that although the 120 years life is called up with regard to structural actions there is no specific reference in the concrete bridge design code for this period for durability. Other values of design life may be encountered for a variety of reasons.

## CURRENT STATE-OF-ART IN SERVICE LIFE DESIGN

A recent RILEM report (Sara and Vesikari, 1996), Concrete Society Discussion Document (Concrete Society, 1996) and two BRE Reports (Marsh, 1996; Bourke and Davies, 1996) provide a useful summary of the state-of-art. The RILEM report represents a significant step forward as it is presented in the form of a design guide although it is questionable whether the mathematical models for the deterioration mechanisms considered are yet sufficiently reliable; indeed they are presented only as examples. The report suggests the following durability design procedure:

1. Specification of the required service life and choice of design life.
2. Analysis of environmental exposure conditions.
3. Identification of degradation factors and deterioration mechanisms.
4. Selection of a durability calculation model for each deterioration mechanism.
5. Calculation of durability design parameters using available calculation models.

6.    Possible updating of the calculations of the structural design (eg self weight).
7.    Transfer of the durability design parameters into the final design.

The BRE Report by Bourke and Davies (1997) describes a factorial approach, whereby the performance of an element or structure is predicted from a Standard Service Life. This is modified by the application of coefficients to take account of positive and negative factors such as quality, design, workmanship, environment, service conditions and maintenance. The resulting prediction of service life is then compared with the required service life. The method is proposed for use in the ISO service life standard under development and is based on a Japanese method (AIJ, 1993). The report concludes that 'a factorial approach would facilitate assessment of the risks of deterioration and be a reasoned response to those risks. While the durability assessment would not be wholly reliable in the absence of further research data it would form a considered and objective assessment and a basis of comparison with alternative options or design solutions'.

Whilst this technique might be suitable for manufactured products such as housing components, its applicability to a bespoke material such as reinforced concrete is questionable. Even if a suitable Standard Service Life could be agreed, there is probably insufficient information available in a suitable form to do more than base the coefficients on a qualitative assessment of each of the influences. There is a fear that the resulting service life prediction, because it appears as a precise value, would assume an authority not supported by the reliability of the assumptions used to produce it, and be adopted without due consideration. This method does, however, have an advantage over many service life design techniques insomuch as it does not rely on specific deterioration models and is able to take some account of effects such as workmanship.

## LIMITATIONS OF CURRENT APPROACHES
A major problem is currently presented by the assessment of the likely durability of a structure where the results from cube tests indicate non-compliance with the specification. For structural purposes we are able to estimate the actual strength from core tests or non-destructive testing and re-assess the structure against the design loads. For durability, however, we are in a much more difficult position. It might be possible to determine the cement content, and even obtain an estimate of the water/cement ratio for Portland cement concrete, although this is virtually impossible for cements containing pfa or ggbs. These values can then be compared with the specification which, if the cube results were reliable, will almost inevitably indicate that the concrete is of lower quality than required by the appropriate standard. Without any indication of how design life is affected by parameters such as water/cement ratio, it is not then possible to make an objective judgement of the likely durability performance of the structure.

Further problems are created by the current systems for classification of environmental exposure, such as that in BS8110. They are insufficiently specific in terms of degradation factors and are only quantitative in the broadest sense. The system proposed for the new European Standards is a step forward as the classification is made directly in terms of the deterioration mechanisms that are to be resisted. Degree of severity of the exposure is, however, mainly qualitative. The difficulties of quantification are illustrated by the attempt in the Concrete Society Discussion Document (Concrete Society, 1996) to relate the degrees of severity of the carbonation-induced corrosion class to average atmospheric relative humidities:

Table 2:    An attempt by the Concrete Society to quantify the prEN206 carbonation-induced corrosion exposure class

| Exposure class | Range of average relative humidities, % | UK example |
|---|---|---|
| XC1: dry, low risk of corrosion | ≤ 65 | Indoor, air conditioned |
| XC2: wet, rarely dry | 91 to 100 | Some buried foundations |
| XC3: moderate humidity | 66 to 74 | In some residential buildings |
| XC4: cyclic wet and dry | 75 to 90 | Outside |

Although this represents a brave attempt at quantification, the humidity ranges are based more on the quoted examples than on a scientific relationship between relative humidity and deterioration. Indeed, the translation of the XC4 'cyclic wet and dry' condition into a band of average relative is contrary to the intention of the exposure class. The severity of this exposure is high because of the wetting and drying which mean the concrete regularly experiences the conditions most conducive to both carbonation and reinforcement corrosion. A reasonably constant high relative humidity environment will not be as severe as many typical cyclic wetting and drying conditions, except perhaps in a particular very narrow relative humidity range.

Another limitation stems from the time currently spent on durability design which is often small compared to that spent on the structural design. It will, however, tend to depend upon the designer's perception of the severity of the environment. With an offshore structure, for example, a designer is likely to instinctively spend a significant time deliberating on durability. In the case of a building, this is much less likely even though the required service life of the building may be longer than that of the offshore structure. Recognition of the issue of service life by the designer is an important step, probably as important as the detail of the solution.

## NEED FOR FUTURE WORK
Although this list is far from comprehensive, the development of satisfactory service life design procedures is dependent upon increased knowledge at least in the areas of:
- Quantification of environmental exposure conditions
- Combined degradation factors
- The conditions controlling the initiation of corrosion

Improved guidance will be required at least in the areas of:
- When service life design is beneficial or necessary
- Specific design procedures
- Defining the end of service life

## AN EXAMPLE OF SERVICE LIFE DESIGN IN PRACTICE
Although described in more detail elsewhere (Ryalls, Cather and Stevens, 1990), the design of the new British Library posed the problem of constructing for an extended life in the region of 500 years. It was assumed that sulfates would attack the concrete piles to a depth of up to 150mm so they were designed, structurally, as 1500mm diameter but built as 1800mm diameter with 235mm cover to the reinforcement. Precast concrete boot lintels which were expected to be in

permanently adverse conditions, and which could not be inspected in use, were designed using stainless steel reinforcement in the most exposed part and with low permeability concrete for the whole unit. This was achieved using a Portland cement concrete of 0.35 maximum water/cement ratio, 330kg/m³ minimum cement content and 7 days of 100% humidity curing by shrink wrapping. This is an example where the requirement for a particularly long service life caused the designers to examine the problem in depth and, in the absence of suitable specific guidance or design methods, select a solution based directly on the nature of the problem.

## CONCLUSIONS

1. Most current UK and worldwide standards and codes of practice for concrete structures contain little or no reference to the concept of designing for a specific life.

2. Development of Eurocodes, European Standards and an ISO design guide is causing attention to be focussed on service life design.

3. Guidance is being developed within CEN, RILEM and ISO that will aid designers in their approach to designing for a specific life.

4. Reliable design procedures which enable the design of concrete structures for precise lives are unlikely in the near future because of the uncertainty of the many variables affecting service life; indeed it may never be possible to achieve the perfected system we crave. Flagging up the issue of service life design principles should, however, increase awareness of the important factors and increase the probability of a specific minimum service life being achieved.

5. The limitations of any service life design technique should never be forgotten.

## REFERENCES

AIJ, 1993, 'Principal guide for service life planning of buildings', English Edition, Architectural Institute of Japan.

Beeby, A W, 1993, 'Design for life', Concrete 2000 - Economic and durable concrete through excellence, Vol 1, Ed. R K Dhir and M R Jones, E & F N Spon, pp 37-50.

Bourke, K and Davies, H, 1997, 'Factors affecting service life predictions of buildings: a discussion paper', Building Research Establishment Laboratory Report BR320, Construction Research Communications Ltd., London.

BS 5400 : Part 4, 1990, 'Steel, concrete and composite bridges. Part 4. Code of practice for design of concrete bridges', British Standards Institution, London.

BS 6349 : Part 1, 1984, 'British Standard Code of Practice for Maritime Structures. Part 1. Code of Practice for General Criteria', British Standards Institution, London.

BS 7543, 1992, 'Guide to durability of buildings and building elements, products and components', British Standards Institution, London.

BS 8110 : Part 1, 1985, 'Structural use of concrete. Part 1. Code of Practice for design and construction', British Standards Institution, London.

BS 8110 : Part 1, 1997, 'Structural use of concrete. Part 1. Code of Practice for design and construction', British Standards Institution, London.

BSI, 1997, 'Draft revision of BS6349 : Part 1 : 1984. Maritime Structures. Part 1. Code of Practice for General Criteria', British Standard Draft for Public Comment 97/102565, London.

Concrete Society, 1996, 'Developments in Durability Design & Performance-Based Specification of Concrete', Discussion Document, Concrete Society Special Publication CS109.

ENV 1991-1, 1994, 'Eurocode 1 : Basis of design and actions on structures. Part 1 : Basis of design', European Prestandard, European Committee for Standardization, Brussels.

ISO, 1995, 'Guide for Service Life Design of Buildings. Part 1 - General Principles', International Organization for Standardization, unpublished committee draft (Private Communication).

Marsh, B K, 1993, 'A summary of European concreting practice', Building Research Establishment Occasional Paper OP53.

Marsh, B K, 1996, 'A review of Service Life Design of concrete structures', Building Research Establishment Literature Review BR316, Construction Research Communications Ltd., London.

O'Brien, T, Cather, R and Figg, J, 1987, 'Concrete durability: the interface between research and practice', Concrete Durability, Katharine and Bryant Mather International Conference, ACI SP100, Detroit, pp 255-264.

prEN206, 1997, 'Concrete - Performance, Production and Conformity', British Standard Draft for Public Comment 97/104685, British Standards Institution, London.

Rowe, R E et al, 1987, 'Handbook to British Standard BS8110:1985. Structural Use of Concrete', Palladian Publications, London.

Ryalls, P J, Cather, R and Stevens, 1990, A, 'Aspects of design for durability at the British Library, 'Protection of Concrete, Ed. R K Dhir and J W Green, E & F N Spon, pp 549-559.

Sara, A and Vesikari, E, 1996, Durability Design of Concrete Structures. RILEM Report 14, E&FN Spon, London.

# Probabilistic Performance Based Durability Design of Concrete Structures

DR PHIL BAMFORTH PhD, CEng, MICE
Taywood Engineering Ltd., Southall, Middlesex, UK

## SYNOPSIS

The paper describes a new probabilistic approach to durability design which is being developed under the Brite-Euram programme. The DuraCrete project is described in relation to the breakdown of tasks, the participating organisations from six EC member states and current progress.

The probabilistic performance based approach to durability design of concrete structures is described and compared with the current approach to structural design. Examples are given of reliability functions which define the probability of achieving a specified design life. The importance of defining serviceability limit states is discussed in relation to the functional requirements of the structure, or an element of the structure, and some limit states are proposed for deterioration caused by corrosion of reinforcement. Reliability functions relating to specific limit states are then given.

The probabilistic approach requires the prediction of service life and mathematical modelling is an essential feature of the methodology. Mathematical models for some of the processes leading to deterioration are described and the importance of taking into account variability, both in the exposure condition and in the resistance of the concrete, is quantified by predicting and comparing typical and characteristic design lives.

## OBJECTIVES

The objectives of this paper are as follows;-

i) to raise awareness of the need for a more rigorous approach to durability design

ii) to describe the Duracrete project in relation to its objectives, task breakdown, participants and progress.

iii) to describe the basic theory of probabilistic design and how it can be applied to durability

iv) to increase awareness of the need to define service life and serviceability limit states relating to durability

v) to describe some of the mathematical models which can be used for prediction of service life

*Management of concrete structures for long-term serviceability.* Thomas Telford, London, 1997

## INTRODUCTION

Concrete is recognised as a variable material and, for structural design, both the inherent variability of concrete and the uncertainties in defining the loading conditions are taken into account. The probability of failure is maintained at an acceptably low level (about $10^{-4}$) by using partial safety factors to ensure that a characteristically 'low' strength (or resistance) exceeds a characteristically 'high' load by an acceptably large margin[1].

For durability, current codes used a deemed-to-satisfy approach. Limits are given for w/c, strength grade, cement content and cover, and if these requirements are met, the structure is deemed 'durable', i.e., it will achieve an acceptably long, but often unspecified service life. If the observed occurrence of premature deterioration was low, then this approach would have to be considered acceptable. However, corrosion of reinforcement continues to represent the single largest cause of deterioration of r.c. structures. The problem is variously attributed to inadequate specification, poor design detailing and construction defects, such as poor compaction or curing or low cover. However, field data suggests that, in the most aggressive exposure conditions, there is an unacceptably high risk of premature deterioration even when the code requirements are met [2] . This is not to say that all structures designed using current codes will deteriorate prematurely, only that the extent of premature deterioration and the associated cost of repairs will continue to be unacceptably high.

To minimise the risk of premature deterioration, an approach is proposed which is similar to that used in structural design. This requires acceptance of the fact that variability, similar to that for mechanical behaviour, also exists in relation to the properties of concrete which influence durability. Furthermore, the inherent variability of the exposure condition or 'environmental loading' on the structure must also be taken into account.

A European collaborative project, DuraCrete, is underway with the objective of developing a probabilistic, performance based, durability design methodology. This methodology is based upon realistic environmental and material models capable of predicting the time dependent behaviour of concrete structures with defined levels of risk and in relation to various serviceability limit states e.g., onset of reinforcement corrosion, cracking and spalling, loss of steel section, or loss of structural integrity. The methodology will be applicable to the design of new concrete structures and for the evaluation of the residual service life of existing structures. The project is being co-ordinated by CUR, in the Netherlands, with partners in the Denmark, Germany, Netherlands, Spain, Sweden and UK,  It began in February 1996 and is due for completion in January 1999.

## THE DURACRETE PROJECT

The project is being undertaken as eight tasks as shown in Figure 1. The twelve partners in the project include Contractors, Consulting Engineers, Research Institutions and Clients Organisations. Table 1 list the partners, summarises their role and identifies where technical input is being made. Most partners are involved in several tasks and there is a high level of interaction.

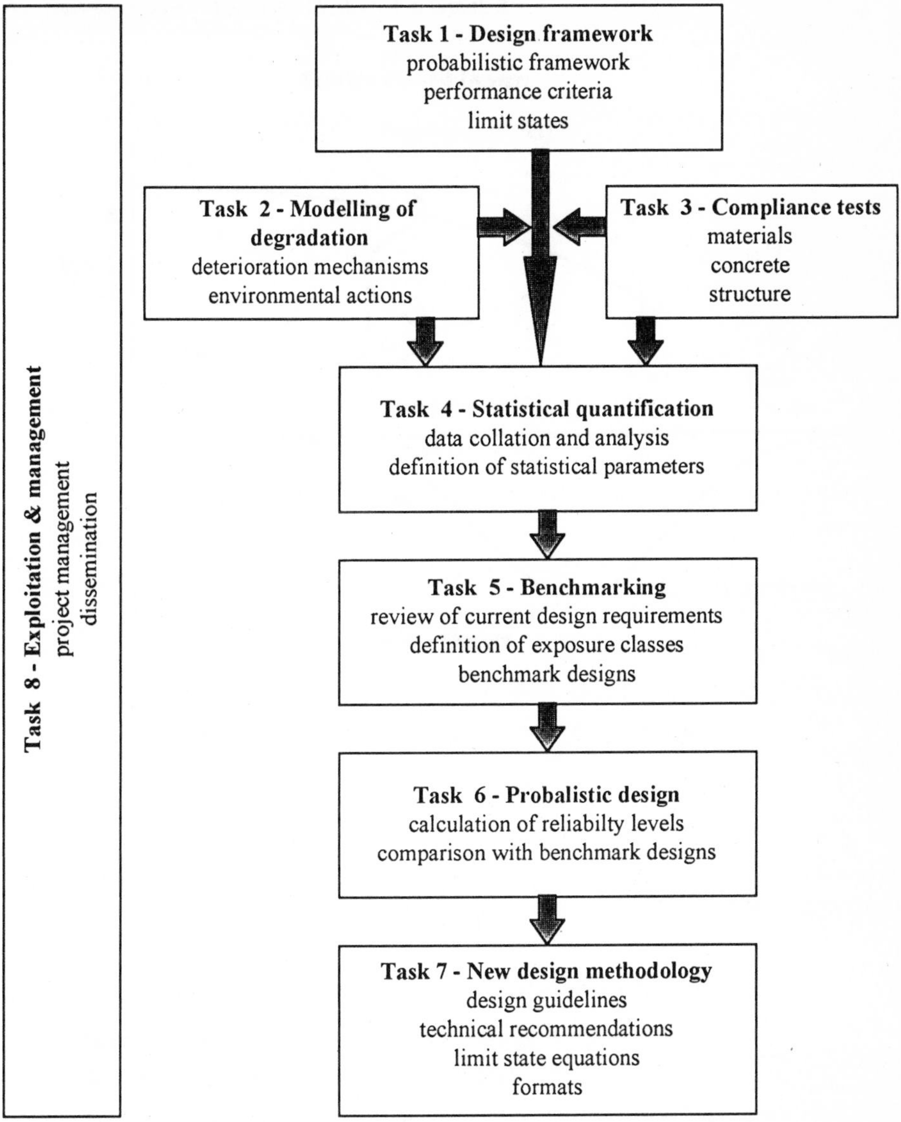

**Figure 1**  *The task breakdown for the DuraCrete project*

**Table 1**  *Partners in the Duracrete project and their involvement in task activities*

| Organisation | Country | Function | Task input |
|---|---|---|---|
| CUR | Netherlands | DURACRETE co-ordinator | 8 |
| Cowi Consulting Engineers | Denmark | Scientific management, task 1 and task 7 leader | 1,3,4,5,6, 7 |
| HBG | Netherlands | Exploitation management | 1,3,4,5,7, 8 |
| Taywood Engineering Ltd | UK | Task 2 and task 5 leader | 2,3,4,5,6, 7 |
| E. Schwenk Zementwerke KG | Germany | | 3,4 |
| Geotecnica y Cimientos, SA (Geocisa), | Spain | | 2,5,7 |
| Institute of Building Research, Aachen (IBAC) | Germany | Task 3 leader | 2,3,4,5,7 |
| Eduardo Torroja Institute of Construction Science | Spain | | 2,4,5,7 |
| RWS, Civil Engineering Division | Netherlands | | 1,5,6 |
| TNO | Netherlands | Task 4 and task 6 leader | 1,4,6,7 |
| Intron | Netherlands | | 2,3,5 |
| Chalmers University of Technology | Sweden | | 2,4,5,6,7 |

Taywood Engineering Ltd (TEL) has an input to six of the eight tasks and is leading task 2, Modelling of Degradation, and task 5, Benchmarking.

The project is currently at about its mid point. Tasks 1 and 2 are largely complete and substantial progress has been made in tasks 3 to 5. These tasks provide the elements of the probabilistic design method which are brought together in tasks 6 and 7.

## PERFORMANCE BASED DURABILITY DESIGN
### Approach
The proposed approach for durability design is similar to that used in structural design[3,4]. In its simplest form this is presented as a limit state function of the form;-

$$R(t) - S(t) \geq 0 \tag{1}$$

where $R(t)$ is the resistance and $S(t)$ is the load, and both are assumed to be time dependent. For structural design it is usual to assume that the strength remains constant and that the loads, even if fluctuating, can be characterized by a single value. In each case partial safety factors are applied to take account of variability and uncertainties, leading to the design values.

Durability is, by definition, time dependent and hence these simplifying assumptions cannot be made. Furthermore, there may be several serviceability limit states. Siemes and Rostam[4] have described two approaches to durability based on the 'intended service period design' and the 'lifetime design'. These are illustrated in Figure 2.

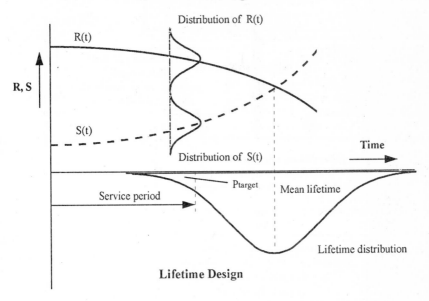

**Figure 2**   *Service period design and lifetime design*[3]

The reliability functions are as follows:

*Intended service period design*

$$P_{f,T} = P\{R(t) - S(t) < 0\}_T \le P_{target} = \Phi(-\beta) \qquad (2)$$

where $P_{f,T}$ is the probability of failure within the intended service period, T

$P_{target}$ is the accepted maximum value of the probability of failure

$\Phi$ is the standard normal distribution function

$\beta$ is the reliability index (normally given in codes instead of the failure probability) and is the number of Standard Deviations from the mean of a normal distribution outside which the area under the curve represents the probability of failure. It can be obtained from tables[1] and the relationship is as follows:-

| $-\beta$ | 1.3 | 2.3 | 3.1 | 3.7 | 4.2 | 4.7 |
|----------|-----|-----|-----|-----|-----|-----|
| $P_{f,T}$ | $10^{-1}$ | $10^{-2}$ | $10^{-3}$ | $10^{-4}$ | $10^{-5}$ | $10^{-6}$ |

*Lifetime design*

$$L = T\{R,S\} \quad \text{where L is the life of the structure} \tag{3}$$

and $\quad P_f = P\{L < T\} \leq P_{target} = \Phi(-\beta)$ \hfill (4)

Each of these approaches uses the same information and will lead to the same result.

For structural design, the risk of failure must be very low. For example, for ultimate limit state (i.e. collapse), Eurocode 1 is based on a probability, $P_{target}$, $= 7 \times 10^{-5}$ ($\beta = 3.8$) for $T = 50$ years. While for structural purposes a low level of the risk of failure is essential for safety reasons, a higher level of risk may be tolerated in relation to serviceability limit states. The consequences are much less severe in relation to safety as there is generally a visual warning long before the defect has serious safety implications, with the opportunity for intervention to reinstate the structure and to prevent further damage. There are cost implications, however, and for this reason the risk of corrosion should still be designed at an acceptably low level. A probability of the onset of corrosion of $10^{-2}$ ($-\beta = 2.3$) may be more appropriate.

## Serviceability Limit States
A critical feature of durability design is the definition of serviceability limit states. These will vary depending upon the nature of the structure and the criticality of specific elements. For corrosion of reinforcement, the following limit states are commonly used;-

i)    *Onset of corrosion* - the time to the onset of corrosion is defined as the Initiation Phase.   Initiation is most commonly deemed to have occurred either when the threshold chloride level is reached or when the concrete has carbonated to the depth of reinforcement,  but it can also be defined by the time to exceed a defined rate of corrosion.   In conditions in which pitting can occur the engineer may decide that no corrosion is acceptable and hence specify the service life to be the onset of corrosion. Using this limit requires either the prediction of chloride ingress and comparison with a selected threshold value or the prediction of carbonation depth and comparison with cover. Functions defining the probability, $P_{IT}$, of Initiation after time T are, therefore, of the form;-

For chlorides, $\quad P_{LT} = \{C_x(t) - C_{th}(t) < 0\}_T \leq 10^{-2}$ \hfill (5)

where $C_x$ is the chloride level at the reinforcement
and $\quad C_{th}$ is the chloride threshold level for corrosion

For carbonation, $\quad P_{LT} = \{X_c(t) - X_r < 0\}_T \leq 10^{-2}$ \hfill (6)

where $X_c$ is the carbonation depth
and $\quad X_r$ is the cover to reinforcement

ii)    *Time to first cracking* - this is usually the time at which some intervention is made. Very little corrosion (less than 100 microns) is needed to cause cracking[5]. Using this limit requires the prediction of the rate of chloride ingress, the consequential rate of corrosion and the amount of corrosion required to cause damage. Alternatively, if there is sufficient experience with structures in a particular environment, a predetermined propagation period may be used. It must be appreciated, however, that in using this approach the designer is allowing corrosion to occur and relying on achieving a predicted period of propagation. If there is a risk of pitting corrosion with rapid loss of steel section, or if the consequences of a spall may be catastrophic e.g. a small piece of concrete falling from a bridge through the windscreen of a car travelling at high speed or from a building onto a passing pedestrian, then caution must be exercised.

iii)    In remote structures it may be acceptable to design to allow a *specified loss of section*. This would only be appropriate, however, where the consequence spalling are acceptable. In practice, except for temporary or non-critical structures in remote locations, it is not expected that this approach is likely to be adopted.

## REQUIREMENTS FOR THE PREDICTION OF LONG TERM PERFORMANCE
### General models for Predicting Deterioration
Most deterioration processes in concrete can be defined by a two stage process, Initiation and Propagation[6] as shown in Figure 3.

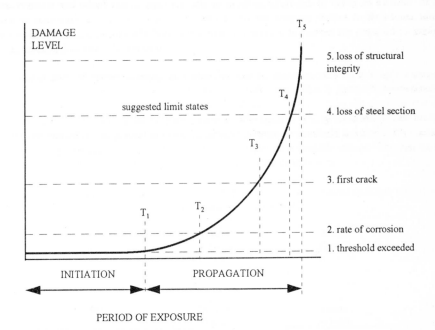

**Figure 3** *The general deterioration model*

As presented in Figure 3 the general model applies to reinforcement corrosion, with the Initiation period defining the time at which either carbonation or chlorides (in excess of the threshold level) causes depassivation of the steel. In the propagation stage the steel is corroding, probably at an increasing rate. However, the same approach can be adopted for other deterioration mechanisms, such as freeze-thaw or alkali aggregate reaction. In these cases the initiation period may be the time to achieve a critical level of saturation or moisture content.

## Mathematical Models

While general models are useful for defining the problem and the critical parameters, to design a structure with a quantifiable service life it is necessary to develop a mathematical model for the mechanism(s) of deterioration. For concrete, all of the deterioration mechanisms are complex interactions of physical and chemical processes. A scientifically based model to predict such complex and varying phenomena, even if achievable conceptually, would be extremely difficult to define mathematically and to execute quantitatively. Moreover, the extensive input data required to validate and operate complex multi-variable models are not currently available and are unlikely to become available due to the level of detail required.

At the opposite end of the spectrum, simple empirical models based on a large number of observations may not be sufficiently flexible to deal with conditions outside the scope of the data used in developing the model. From an engineering point of view, it is desirable that models, whilst being sufficiently accurate, are relatively easy to use, relying on mathematical formulations which do not require complex numerical methods of solution, and input data which can be obtained from laboratory or field tests that are relatively fast, easy and economical to perform. Such input data is also subject to uncertainty and it is not surprising, therefore, that the majority of models currently available for design purposes rely on a compromise being achieved, being scientifically based, but using simplifying assumptions to make them acceptable to practising engineers. At the very least a deterioration model must include terms that represent the environmental loading and the resistance offered by the concrete, and all terms must be measurable.

## Model for Chloride Ingress into Concrete

As an example, for predicting the ingress of chlorides into concrete the following equation is proposed:

$$x = 2 \cdot C \sqrt{f_t \cdot D_{ca(m)} \cdot f_c \cdot f_e \cdot t \cdot \left(\frac{t_m}{t}\right)^n} \qquad (7)$$

in which,     $C = \mathrm{erf}^{-1}\left(1 - \frac{C_x}{C_{sa}}\right)$ \qquad (8)

and:    $D_{ca(m)}$    is the apparent diffusion coefficient measured at time $t_m$

$C_{sn}$    is the surface chloride level

$C_x$    is the level of chloride at depth x

n    is the age factor;

$f_t$, $f_c$ and $f_e$ are constants which take account of the method of test, curing and environment, respectively.

The above equations 7 and 8 include parameters for defining the environmental loading, $C_{sn}$, the resistance of the cover concrete, x, $D_{ca}$ and n, and is based on diffusion theory, being a solution to Fick's second law of diffusion. The values $C_{sn}$, $D_{ca}$ and n can be determined by analysis of chloride profiles obtained from structures or field trials, or from laboratory tests. The constants can be derived from observations and analysis of data. To develop this equation it has been necessary to make the following simplifying assumptions;

i)   Chloride ingress is principally by diffusion - while chloride ingress, in reality involves a complex interaction of mechanisms (absorption, diffusion, binding), in many conditions the shape of the observed chloride profile can be fitted using diffusion theory and in the long term, as chlorides penetrate deeper, diffusion becomes the dominant mechanism.

ii)  Spatial and temporal changes in the resistance of the concrete can be accommodated using the age factor, n.

iii) The surface chloride level remains constant after initial exposure - in the most severe exposure conditions this has been observed[7] while in less severe conditions, where it may build up more slowly, it represents a safe assumption.

While the model has limitations it provides a basis for predictions which are consistent with observations and which can be used for new or existing structures to make an estimate of the time to corrosion activation. It also provides a tool for scoping studies to determine which factors are most critical and which combinations of concrete and cover are required to achieve an acceptably low risk of corrosion.

The importance of taking account of variability can be demonstrated by a simple example. Consider an element of a coastal structure in the splash zone. This is generally recognised as one of the most severe exposure conditions and current UK codes require the use of a low w/c ratio concrete (0.45) with a high cement content (400 kg/m$^3$). Using equation 7, calculations have been carried out to predict the time to achieve a chloride threshold level of 0.4% (cement weight) using both typical values of $C_{sn}$ an $D_{ca}$ and upper 80 percentile values. The results are given in Table 2, together with the assumptions used in the calculations.

**Table 2** *Calculation of time to corrosion activation for portland cement concrete with a w/c of 0.45 in a marine environment*

| Cover depth (mm) | Typical (Case 1) $C_{sn} = 0.36$ $D_{ca} = 9.4 \times 10^{-13}$ m$^2$/s $n = -0.264$ | Design (Case 2) $C_{sn} = 0.58$ $D_{ca} = 1.47 \times 10^{-12}$ m$^2$/s $n = -0.264$ |
|---|---|---|
| 25 | 4 years | 1 year |
| 50 | 26 years | 9 years |
| 75 | 77 years | 26 years |

The typical case represents a probability of about 0.2, while the design case has a probability of about $10^{-2}$. The predicted times to activation for these two cases differ by 3 to 4 times. Current codes generally require 50mm cover and the calculations suggest that there is a 1 in 100 chance of corrosion being initiated within 9 years and a 1 in 5 chance that initiation will occur within 26 years.

## Model for Carbonation of Concrete

A model for carbonation of concrete is proposed which is very similar to that proposed for chloride ingress. The model has been developed by CEB Task Group V (1+2)[8] and is represented mathematically as follows:-

$$X_c = \sqrt{\frac{2K_1.K_2.D_{eff}.C_s}{a}} \sqrt{t} \left(\frac{t_0}{t}\right)^n \tag{9}$$

in which,    $a = 0.75 \cdot C \cdot c \cdot DH \cdot \dfrac{M_{CO_2}}{M_{CaO}}$    (10)

and    $D_{eff}$    is the effective diffusion coefficient at defined compaction, curing and environmental conditions $(m^2/s)$

   $a$    is the binding capacity for $CO_2$ $(kg\ CO_2/m^3)$

   $C_s$    is the $CO_2$ concentration at the surface $(kg\ CO_2/m^3)$

   $t$    is the time in service $(s)$

   $t_0$    is a reference period, e.g. 1 year $(s)$

   $K_1$,    is a constant parameter which considers the influence of execution of $D_{eff}$ (e.g. influence of curing)

   $K_2$,    is a constant parameter which considers the influence of the environment on $D_{eff}$ (e.g. realistic moisture history at the concrete surface during use)

Again, equations 9 and 10 reflect the important parameters and the input data are all measurable.

## Other models

The above models deal with onset of corrosion. Additional models are used to predict corrosion rates, time to cracking and rate of structural deterioration. Furthermore, while the programme has focused on the principal deterioration mechanism in reinforced concrete structures, namely reinforcement corrosion, attempts are also being made to deal with frost action and alkali aggregate reaction (AAR). The general principles are the same, however, involving assessment of the probability of defined limit states being exceeded. For example, both frost action and AAR require the presence of moisture in sufficient quantities to cause disruption of the concrete. Hence, the probability of initiation, $P_{IT}$, can be defined by the relationship between the actual moisture content, $M_c(t)$, and a critical moisture state, $M_{crit}$, and the probability function may, therefore, be of the form;

$$P_{I,T} = \{M_c(t) - M_{crit} < 0\}_T \leq 10^{-2} \tag{11}$$

The exposure conditions are also being modelled, particularly in relation to the temperature and relative humidity. The time of wetness is also important as all of the deterioration mechanisms are strongly influenced by the degree of saturation of the concrete. This is accommodated within the predictive models using constants for different environments (see equations 7 and 9).

In relation to pavements, a probabilistic approach is also being developed to deal with fatigue.

*Validation*
An essential part of the project involves validation of the proposed models and the definition of the constants for factors such as execution, environment and the method of test. This involves the collection and analysis of a substantial volume of data. For example, a spreadsheet has been established which, currently, includes over 1700 values of chloride diffusion coefficient derived from laboratory tests, exposure trials and field measurements together with background information on the concrete mix proportions and constituents, the method of testing and the exposure conditions. These data have been used to derive age factors for the apparent chloride diffusion coefficient and to relate $D_{ca}$ to water/binder ratio and binder constituents. Similar spreadsheets are being prepared for other critical parameters. Clearly, the more data which can be generated, the greater the confidence in the derived constants and hence the reliability of the predictions obtained using the proposed models.

## CONCLUSIONS
The current approach to durability design is limited in many respects and premature deterioration of reinforced concrete resulting from reinforcement corrosion continues to be a major problem. Codes use a deemed-to-satisfy approach but in many cases fail to define either service life or serviceability limit states relating to durability. It is, therefore, difficult within the current design framework to quantify predicted performance and hence to evaluate the cost-effectiveness of proposed improvements.

The DuraCrete project aims to establish a new approach to durability design which is probabilistic and performance based. This will enable the changing state of a structure to be predicted and the probability of defined durability limit states being exceeded to be quantified. The approach will be applicable to new structures, to enable whole life cost optimisation, and to existing structures, for optimisation of repair and future maintenance.

## ACKNOWLEDGEMENTS
The author wishes to thank the Directors of Taywood Engineering Ltd, the European Commission and the partners in the DuraCrete programme for permission to publish this paper. The DuraCrete project 'Probabilistic Performance Based Durability Design of Concrete Structures' is being carried out within the framework of the Brite-Euram Programme (project BE95-1347) with a financial contribution from the European Commission.

## REFERENCES
1. British Standards Institution, Eurocode 1: Basis of design and action on structures, Part 1: Basis of design (together with United Kingdom National Application Document), DD ENV 1991-1:1996

2. Bamforth, P. B. Predicting the risk of reinforcement in marine structures, Odd E. Gjorv Symposium on Concrete for Marine Structures, 3rd CANMET/ACI Int. Conf. on Performance of Concrete in Marine Environment, New Brunswick, Canada, August 1996, pp. 207-234

3. Siemes, A. J. M., Vrouwenvelder, A. C. W. M. and van den Beukel, Durability of buildings: a reliability analysis, HERON, Vol. 30, No. 3, 1985.

4. Siemes, A. J. M. and Rostam, S., Durability, safety and serviceability - A performance based design, TNO report no 96-BT-R0437-001, Feb 1996, (presented at the IABSE

Colloquium 'Basis of Design and Actions on Structures' Delft, Netherlands, March 27-29, 1996)

5.    Bamforth, P. B.   Definition of exposure classes and concrete mix requirements for chloride contaminated environments,  4th Int. Symp. on Corrosion of Reinforcement in Concrete Construction, Society of Chemical Industry, Cambridge, UK, July 1996, pp 176-190.

6.    Tuutti, K.   Corrosion of steel in concrete,  Report Fo 4.82, Swedish Cement and Concrete Association, Stockholm, 1982.

7.    Rodriguez, J., Ortga, L. M., Casal, J. and Diez, J. M.   Corrosion of reinforcement and service life of structures, Int. Conf. on Durability of Building Materials and Components, Stockholm, 1996.

8.    CEB TG V/1+2, Service life design for concrete structures, 2nd draft, 1996.

# Durable Concrete Structures In The Extreme Environment Of The Middle East

DAVID SLATER CEng, MICE, MIStructE; DON WIMPENNY MPhil, CEng, MIM and DR WILLIAM TONER PhD
Materials Technology Unit, Sir William Halcrow & Partners Ltd, Swindon and London, England

## SYNOPSIS
In order to produce durable reinforced concrete structures in extreme environments, it is necessary to apply our experience of the performance of similar structures under comparable conditions and to understand the main factors which control deterioration processes. We also need to acknowledge the limits of our understanding, particularly when a very long service life is required, and to plan long-term monitoring and maintenance strategies to allow the risk to be managed. By using such an approach, a durability plan can be produced. This paper outlines the methods adopted for producing durability plans for the construction of new structures, with particular reference to the hot, saline conditions in the Middle East. A risk register approach is proposed for producing a formalised and efficient methodology for future durability plans.

## OBJECTIVES
The objectives of this paper are to outline the main stages of durability planning for reinforced concrete structures in extreme environments, with particular reference to hot, saline environments, and to introduce the potential benefits of the risk register approach for future development.

Durability planning has four main stages, viz:
- assessment of the performance requirements and the exposure conditions detailed consideration of the likely deterioration processes at different parts of the works
- recommendations for improving durability by appropriate design, specification, detailing and construction methods and practices
- long-term monitoring and maintenance strategy for the completed works.

## PERFORMANCE REQUIREMENTS AND EXPOSURE CONDITIONS
The owner in conjunction with the designer must first determine the operational service life and functional requirements for the individual elements or the entire structure. The designer must then choose a target or design service life for the structure, this being *"the assumed period for which a structure is to be used for its intended purpose with anticipated maintenance but without major repair being necessary."*[1] The target service life will exceed the operational service life to give a safety factor. This safety factor should be adjusted to allow for differing levels of uncertainty and risk, eg poorly defined exposure conditions, exacting performance requirements, high consequential cost of premature deterioration or failure.

*Management of concrete structures for long-term serviceability.* Thomas Telford, London, 1997

Once the design working life has been determined, the next task is to assess the exposure conditions both during construction and in service. The exposure conditions can vary significantly between different parts of a structure and will determine the most critical deterioration process for each element. The exposure conditions are most importantly defined by the temperature, moisture conditions and the exposure to water-soluble salts (in particular, chlorides and sulfates). Temperature influences the rate of chemical and diffusion processes within concrete and the subsequent corrosion of the embedded steel. The moisture conditions in the concrete, arising from ambient humidity, rainfall and wetting and drying greatly influence the rate of carbonation and chloride ingress and the availability of moisture and oxygen for reinforcement corrosion.

By using first-hand and reported experience of the deterioration of actual structures in similar service conditions, the designer can identify the locations where environmental exposure will be most critical to the durability performance of each element of the structure for both the short-term construction condition and the in-service conditions.The short-term conditions are important because they can be more severe than the in-service conditions and may adversely affect the long-term durability.

An example of the deterioration processes identified for a water-conveying tunnel is shown in Figure 1.

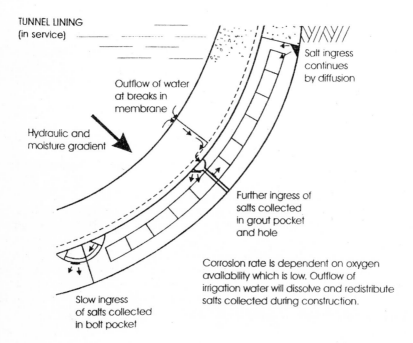

**Figure 1 Deterioration Processes for a Water-Conveying Tunnel Lining in Service**

## DETERIORATION PROCESSES AND MODELS

### Deterioration Processes

The next step is to translate the exposure conditions into deterioration processes and models. The deterioration processes fall into three categories, namely physical degradation of the concrete, chemical attack of the concrete, and corrosion of steel reinforcement and embedments.

Physical degradation can be caused by a number of mechanisms, including: scaling of the concrete surface due to the crystallisation of salts within the capillary pores; abrasion and impact damage due to traffic movement, passage of water and suspended particles, and the sliding or dropping of heavy objects.

Chemical attack can take a variety of forms, including: acid attack, softwater leaching, sulfate attack, alkali-agregate reactions and attack by industrial chemicals, eg ammonium salts from the fertiliser industry[3].

Corrosion of steel reinforcement and embedments is the biggest cause of premature deterioration and failure of reinforced concrete structures. The key mechnisms are carbonation and chloride ingress, although corrosion may also occur at cracks originating from chemical attack and physical degradation. In this respect, the deterioration processes are not strictly independent of each other.

### General Models

Ideally, the quantitative durability model should include the environmental and mechanical loading on the structure and should be carried out in probabilistic terms for corrosion damage, mechanical loading and allow for stochastic variations in the environmental conditions and the quality of workmanship (eg cover depth).[4,5].

The above approach is difficult to implement because of the need for detailed long-term data to provide the statistical parameters. A pragmatic alternative, applied in many other aspects of engineering design, is the derivation of simple design models based upon broad experience from the performance of real structures. These simple durability design models are intended to provide a deterministic method of selecting the appropriate materials properties and depth of cover to achieve the required service life under the exposure conditions. These models can be used alongside the usual deterministic structural design method.

### Physical Degradation and Chemical attack

There appear to be few published models for the rates of physical degradation and chemical attack[6]. The emphasis has been to establish severity ratings for different environments with guidance on appropriate mix selection [7,8].

In general, physical degradation and chemical attack due to naturally occurring substances tends to cause significant deterioration much more slowly than corrosion of reinforcement. Consequently, problems due to chemical attack are less widespread than those due to corrosion of the reinforcement and there is little published quantifiable data available from real structures to help the designer calculate rates of attack. Experiments to compare the performance of different concrete mixes have usually accelerated the deterioration by adopting artificially severe conditions and so only provide a qualitative measure.

A simplistic method of allowing for physical and chemical degradation is to estimate a loss of section and then make an appropriate increase in the section thickness or cover.

### Reinforcement corrosion

The widely accepted model of reinforcement corrosion is the 2-phase model proposed by Tuutti[9] as shown in Figure 2. This indicates a period of initiation of corrosion, $t_i$, due to carbonation or chloride penetration, followed by a period of corrosion. The corrosion causes increasing damage which after a propagation time $t_p$ require repair in order to maintain the serviceability of the structure. The target service life, t, is the sum of the initiation period and the propagation period and the modelling problem becomes one of determining times $t_i$ and $t_p$.

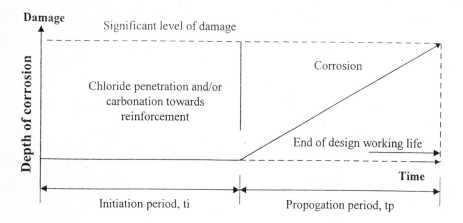

**Figure 2     The Tuutti 2-phase model of reinforcement corrosion[9]**

Several simplifications to the Tuutti model are commonly employed:
- assume that $t_p$ is negligible and the service life is the time to initiation of corrosion
- assume that $t_i$ is negligible and the service life is determined by the time for corrosion to generate significant damage, eg spalling
- ignore the separate phases and model on the basis of a single rate of deterioration based on observed service lives

All the above methodologies have been applied by the authors and have been found to have limitations. In particular, the first approach is not in accordance with the principal author's experience from detailed investigations of maritime structures over the past 20 years in the Middle East. Here chloride levels can quickly reach levels of 0.3% Cl by mass of cement, which is considered to be the lower limit of likely corrosion threshold values, but it then takes some years before disruption of concrete cover occurs. The average service lives indicate that for hot dry conditions 8  years can be taken as the time from corrosion initiation until repairs are necessary, with the timescale almost doubling under hot wet conditions because of the inhibiting effect of the moisture within the cover zone. Under temperate and cool with freezing conditions, the effect of lower average temperatures slows the process still further and the easily remembered series of 8 years, 16 years and 32 years has been proposed as the propagation times, $t_p$, for hot dry, hot wet and temperate/cool with freezing climates in the usual range of seawater salinities[10]

## Chloride Ingress

Models which take account of all the moisture transport processes within the pore structure of the concrete, in particular capillary suction after drying, and can allow for adsorption of chloride ions onto the surfaces of the capillaries depending upon the cement type, are still in the development stage.[11,12] Therefore, at present Fick's second law of diffusion is often used to calculate an effective diffusion coefficient which is artificially high due to capillary suction effects. Alternatively, an empirical allowance can be made for the effects of capillary suction in the splash zone in hot dry environments based upon site and laboratory measurements.[13]

To establish the required mix for the minimum depth of cover a best-fit curve can be fitted using the Fick's solution for the critical chloride profile within the cover zone. A surface chloride concentration and threshold chloride level of 3.0% and 0.3% Cl by mass of cement are typically assumed[14,15]. The specified limit for chlorides introduced at mixing can be used to derive the required effective average long-term chloride diffusion coefficient.

The chloride diffusion coefficient can be converted into a water/cement ratio for Portland cement concrete based on published data.[10] If a blended cementitious mix is used, a reduced diffusion coefficient will apply for the same basic water/cement ratio.[15,16] To allow for different average temperatures, the factor on the diffusion coefficient can be adjusted by applying the Arrhenius equation:

$$Factor = \exp\left(\frac{E}{R}\left(\frac{1}{293} - \frac{1}{T + 273}\right)\right)$$

where E is the activation energy, R is the molar gas constant and T is the temperature in degrees Centigrade. Arrhenius adjustment factors are shown in Figure 3.

Predicted chloride ingress for a structure in the Middle East is shown in Figure 4. The designer can trade off increasing cost and potential workmanship/procurement difficulties of the concrete mix cost versus depth of cover.

## Carbonation

A number of models have been developed by various researchers for the rate of ingress of the carbonation front for different concrete mixes.[18,19,20] The agreement between the various models is poor, not least because of differences in the mixes, curing and moisture condition of the concrete . The maximum rate of carbonation occurs at an effective relative humidity of 50% to 60% but drops to a low value outside this range.[3]

An important consideration in some cases is the potential for carbonation to release adsorbed chloride ions from the surface zone and thereby increase chloride concentrations at greater depth. Models to deal with this combined case have been proposed[19].

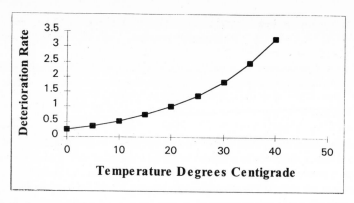

**Figure 3** Comparative rates of deterioration processes at different temperatures based on Arrhenius equation [17]

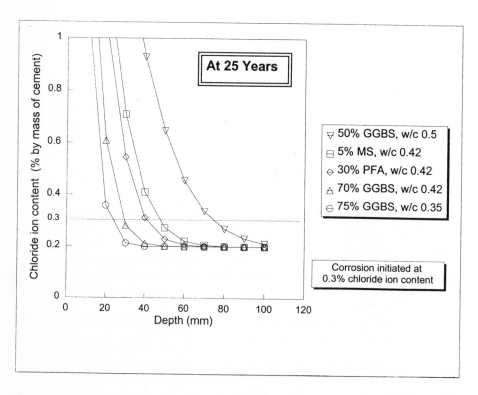

**Figure 4** Predicted chloride ingress for different concrete mixes in a hot saline environment

The predicted carbonation depth for a structure in the Middle East is shown in Figure 5. The relationship is based on the use of slag cement concrete and the higher and lower rates correspond to indoor and outdoor exposure.[18] The rates for coated concrete assume the use of an effective carbonation coating[21].

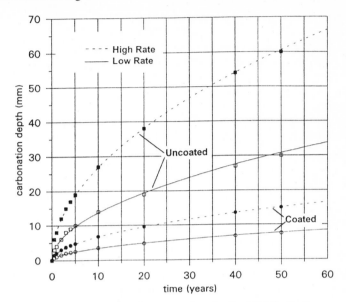

**Figure 5**     **Predicted Carbonation for a structure in the Middle East**

## DURABILITY BY APPROPRIATE DESIGN
Once the critical locations and possible deterioration mechanisms have been identified, it is then possible for the designer to investigate alternative methods of slowing the deterioration to meet the target service life. At this stage, the simple models are used to give a range of options for different concrete mixes, different depths of cover and, possibly, additional measures such as controlled permeability formwork or coatings. It is also possible to identify design details and construction practices which can improve the situation and even reduce expenditure in some areas.

Typical design measures to maximise durability, include:
- making the structure buildable to minimise the risk of workmanship problems
- making the structure easy to inspect and maintain
- careful attention to drainage to control the run-off and ponding of water
- minimising the number of arrises and incorporation of chamfers
- avoiding details which penetrate or prejudice the integrity of the cover zone
- locating construction joints away the severest exposure zones
- use of precast elements

Examples of recommendations from a durability plan prepared for a tunnel in hot desert conditions with high chlorides and sulphates in the ground water are given in Table 1.

| (a) | Excavated material may drain contaminated ground water into the works and the disposal of the material needs to be carefully planned (specification clause required). Excavations should not be left open for any longer than necessary to reduce the risk of salt rich or acidic layers being formed. |
|-----|-----------------------------------------------------------------------------------------------------------------------------------------------------------------------------------------------------------------------------------------------------------------------------------------------------------|
| (b) | Overall durability will be determined by the extent of the lowest quality of the cover concrete coincident with the least depth of cover achieved in practice in the most aggressive micro-climate experienced. Hence, the durability of the structure will be determined by the statistics of workmanship. Close control of the depth of cover achieved in practice, and checked by covermeter after concreting to establish the statistics and confirm the quality, will be the most cost-effective contribution towards durability (site supervision required). |
| (c) | Great care needs to be taken to protect reinforcement from contamination by salts and to thoroughly clean it prior to concreting. Particular care needs to be taken where starter bars are exposed for any length of time (specification clause and site supervision required). |
| (d) | Wherever possible the concrete should be protected from contact with ground water during its early life (specification clause required). Attention should be given to preventing inundations of salty surface run-off water during storm (site supervision required). |
| (d) | The greatest care needs to be exercised to maintain the integrity of the membranes and coatings during construction (specification clause required). The passage of ground water needs to be prevented where a hydraulic gradient or evaporation may promote water movement (site supervision required). |

**Table 1 Examples of recommendations from a durability plan for a Middle East structure**

In situations where a very long service life is required in an extreme environment, the most cost effective approach is often to limit initial capital expenditure by taking prudent steps to slow deterioration processes, making provision for further measures to be adopted at some later date if needed and managing the risk by implementing a monitoring strategy.

### MONITORING AND MAINTENANCE
A monitoring and maintenance strategy allows the assumptions and predictions at the design stage to be confirmed and ensures that maintenance can be correctly timed and targeted.

During construction, information is gathered to confirm the service conditions and the as-built details of the structure. This information could include additional data on the ground conditions, concrete mixes, workmanship defects and design amendments. Following handover, condition surveys will be undertaken at intervals of say 1, 5 and 10 years. The precise survey techniques depend on the access available and the anticipated deterioration mechanisms. The survey would typically involve visual assessment, concrete dust sampling for chloride ingress, measurement of carbonation depth and electro potential mapping for corrosion activity. The condition of inaccessible elements could be judged by remote monitoring using embedded half-cell electrodes and corrosion ladders[22] and/or by inspecting reference elements subject to similar exposure conditions. The data gathered from these surveys should be supplemented by information from the operator to identify any modifications to the service conditions or to the structure which may have an impact upon its durability.

An example of a monitoring system for a water-conveying tunnel in the Middle East is given in Figure 6. The segments were buried alongside the actual structure, in the same environmental conditions, to allow retrieval and inspection.

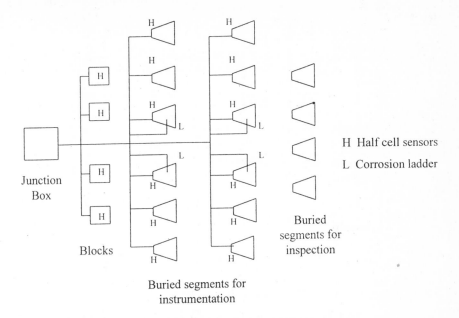

**Figure 6**   **Corrosion monitoring system for a water-conveying tunnel in the Middle East**

A total of 16 no. epoxy coated precast tunnel segments and 4 no. blocks will be used to simulate the primary tunnel lining and surface works concrete, respectively. The tunnel segments will be buried at 3m below ground level, whilst the reinforced concrete blocks will be placed above and below ground level to simulate partially buried conditions The instrumentation comprises manganese dioxide half-cell electrodes and corrosion ladders. Each corrosion ladder is formed from six mild steel anodes at cover values of 10-50mm and a platinum oxide-coated titanium cathode.

## RISK REGISTER APPROACH

For future durability plans, it is proposed that a risk register approach will provide a more formalised and suitable methododology [23]. Examples of tables for a two stage approach are shown in Tables 2 and 3. The first stage will involve identifying the critical environments for each element of the structure, which has an impact on the types of risks considered in the second stage. The second stage then identifies the most significant risks, where further mitigation may be appropriate, and also opportunities for cost savings where the micro-environment is less severe or where elements can have shorter target service lives. For the system to become part of a routine design method, expert guidance in the form of tables of deterioration processes for different environmental conditions with rates of deterioration and alternative solution strategies will be needed. We are working on it!

| CONCRETE DURABILITY RISK ASSESSMENT : STAGE 1 | | | | | Date:<br>Prep. by: | |
|---|---|---|---|---|---|---|
| **Severity Rating for Elements of a Structure** | | | | | Rev:<br>Checked: | |
| **Element &<br>Location** | **Exposure** | **Severity of Deterioration Process** | | | | |
| | | Corrosion due to Carbonation | Corrosion due to Chlorides | Physical weathering | Chemical attack | A<br>A<br>R |
| | Above capillary rise zone, external faces | | | | | |
| | Above capillary rise zone, internal faces | | | | | |
| | Below ground, external faces | | | | | |
| | Below ground, internal faces | | | | | |

**Table 2 Severity Rating Table showing example exposure conditions**

**REFERENCES**
1. CEN (European Committee for Standardisation) (1994) ENV 1991 - 1. Eurocode 1: "*Basis of Design and Actions on Structures. Part 1: Basis of Design*", Brussels.
2. CEB (Comite Euro-international du Beton) (1989) "*Durable Concrete Structures - Design Guide*", Second Edition 1989, Reissued 1992, Thomas Telford Services Ltd.
3. RILEM (1996) "*Durability Design of Concrete Structures*", Ed. Sarja & Vesikari, Report of RILEM Technical Committee 130-CSL, E & FN Spon, London.
4. Bamforth P B. (1995) "*Predicting the Risk of Reinforcement Corrosion in Marine Structures*", (Unpublished at time of private communication).
5.Poole T S. (1994) "*Individual and Combined Effects of Chloride, Sulphate and magnesium ions*", NTIS Report, Sand-93-70404, 1994.
6. Clifton J R. (1993) "*Predicting the service life of Concrete*", ACI Materials Journal, November-December 1993, pp 611-617.
7.Alexandar M, Addis B and Basson J. (1994) "*Case Studies using a novel method to assess aggressiveness of waters to concrete* ", ACI Materials Journal, March-April 1994, pp 188- 196.
8.Gorenbien V YA, "*The Wear Resistance of the Linings of Hydraulic Structures* ", CIRIA Translation 26, Energiya, Moscow, 1967.
9. Tuutti K. (1982) "*Corrosion of steel in concrete*", CBI forskning/research, Swedish Cement and Concrete Research Institute, Stockholm.
10. Allen R T L. (Ed) (1997), "*Concrete in Coastal Structures* ", Chapter 6 "The *design of coastal structures*" by Slater D and Sharp B N, Thomas Telford Publishing (to be published 97)
11. Bijen J M J M. (1995) Personal Communication on the development of the "*Chloride*" Module within the *FEMMASSE* suite of programs.

| CONCRETE DURABILITY RISK ASSESSMENT : STAGE 2 | | Date: | Prep by: |
| RISK and OPPORTUNITY REGISTER | | Rev: | Checked: |

**ELEMENT & LOCATION:**

| Risk Ref No | Risk Description | Proposed Primary Control | Residual Risk Level | | | Possible Further Mitigation |
|---|---|---|---|---|---|---|
| | | | Likeli-hood | Conse-quence | Critic-ality | |
| MATERIALS | | | | | | |
| | Unsuitable materials/ mix design leads to poor quality concrete | Control max w/c ratio, min cementitious content, cement type and early curing methods | | | | |
| CONSTRUCTION METHODS/ WORKMANSHIP | | | | | | |
| | Poor placing and compaction results in low quality concrete | Supervision Ensure high workability by using admixtures | | | | |
| DESIGN DETAILING | | | | | | |
| | Inadequate cover for steel | Add workmanship tolerance to design minimum cover | | | | |
| MONITORING/ MAINTENANCE | | | | | | |
| | Poor monitoring leads to developing damage not being detected immediately | Institute routine inspection and monitoring regime from outset | | | | |

**Table 3    Risk and Opportunity Register, showing example sources of risk**

12. Saetta A V, Scotta R V and Vitaliani RV. (1993) *"Analysis of Chloride Diffusion into Partially Saturated Concrete"* , ACI Materials Journal/ September-October 1993 pp 441-451

13. Slater D. (1992) *"Moisture Profiles in Concrete under Wetting and Drying Regimes"* Confidential Halcrow Report.

14. Chapman-Andrews J. and Bamforth P.B. (1996) *"Definition of exposure classes and concrete mix requirements for chloride contaminated environments."*, 4th SCI Conference on Corrosion of Reinforcement in Concrete Construction, July 1996, Cambridge.

15. Bijen J M. (1985) *"On the durability of Portland Blastfurnace Slag cement Concrete in Hot Marine Environment* ", Proceedings of the 1st International Conference on the deterioration and repair of Reinforced Concrete in the Arabian Gulf, 26-29 October 1985.

16. Gautefall O.E. and Havdahl J. (1989) *"Effect of condensed silica fume on the mechanism of chloride diffusion into hardened cement paste"*, ACI Publication SP114, Vol 2 1989, pp 849-860.

17. Page C.L., Short N.R. and Tarras A.El (1981) *"Diffusion of chloride ions in hardened cement pastes"*, Cement and Concrete Research, Vol 11, pp 395-406.

18. Bijen J van der Wengen G and Selst R,*"Carbonation of Portland Blastfurnace Slag Cement Concrete with Fly Ash"*,ACI Publication SP114, Vol 1, 1989, pp 645-668.

19. Kay E A. (1992) *"Assessment and renovation of concrete structures"*, Longman Scientific and Technical, 1992, ISBN 0582-05779-5, pp133- 136.

20. Hobbs D W (1988),*"Carbonation of concrete containing pfa"*, Magazine of Concrete Research, Vol 40, No 143, June 1988, pp69- 78.

21. Robinson H L. (1986) *" Evaluation of coatings as carbonation barriers"*, Proceedings of the 2nd International Colloquium, Materials Science and Restoration, Esslingen, West Germany, Sept 2-4 , 1986.

22. Raucpach M. (1993)*" Monitoring of corrosion risk for new concrete structures* ", Concrete 2000, Edited by Dhir and Jones, E&FN Spon, Vol 2, ISBN 0 419181202, pp 1265-1273.

23. Godfrey P S G. (1996) *" Control of Risk - A guide to the Systematic Management of Risk from Construction* ", CIRIA Special Publication 125, 1996.

# The Use of Non-Linear Finite Element Analysis in Service Life Predictions for Concrete Structures

DR ROGER S CROUCH [1] DIC, PhD AND PROFESSOR NENAD BICANIC[2] PhD
[1] Senior Lecturer, Department of Civil & Structural Engineering, University of Sheffield
[2] Professor and Head of Department of Civil Engineering, University of Glasgow

## SYNOPSIS
This review article reports on the capability of non-linear finite element analysis (FEA) to help predict the service life of reinforced and pre-stressed concrete structures. After a brief reference to linear FEA, some difficulties in undertaking certain types of non-linear analysis are highlighted. Drawing partly on two State-of-the-Art reports [1] and a recently completed research study [2] it is shown that, despite enormous advances, more work is required before accurate fracture simulations can be made routinely for complex structures. This is particularly true if reliable deformation predictions are to be made up to the point of collapse. Examples of the static and dynamic analysis of real structures are provided to illustrate some of the concepts. The paper goes on to discuss techniques whereby transient thermal loading, moisture diffusion (with associated creep and shrinkage) and electro-chemical deterioration processes may be incorporated into a complete multi-physics solution. The latter have special relevance to the long-term performance of a reinforced concrete structure. The paper concludes with an assessment of future use of non-linear FEA.

## 1. INTRODUCTION TO THE FINITE ELEMENT METHOD
Over the past three decades, finite element analysis has not just been used by the research community but has become the accepted design tool in structural mechanics. Yet, despite the ability of this method to handle many diverse physical phenomena (in addition to mechanical loading) the application of FE to durability problems in complex reinforced concrete structures has only just begun. Given the success of the technique in other branches of engineering and physics, it appears inevitable that the next decade will see, for example, further use of FEA to simulate the time-dependent processes of chloride ingress, carbonation and corrosion of reinforcement. Once the governing mathematical models coupling thermo-mechanical and electro-chemical systems have been properly identified, a common solution approach is possible since all these problems can be expressed by similar integral equations and solved by finite elements. Such analyses will enable predictions of rates of corrosion to be linked to loss of mechanical performance. Other studies, for example, linking moisture removal to restrained shrinkage in repair systems will allow predictions of the likelihood of further cracking to be performed. The progressive growth of fractures in the concrete cover zone (due to cyclic mechanical load or freeze-thaw effects, for example) influences the rate of chloride transport, leading to a faster loss of bond at the steel-concrete interface, more rapid corrosion of the reinforcement and hence a degradation of the sectional moment or force resistance. Since structural integrity is the main issue, then reliable FE modelling of these durability related

*Management of concrete structures for long-term serviceability.* Thomas Telford, London, 1997

phenomena is meaningful only if the load carrying capacity of reinforced concrete (RC) structures (ignoring the diffusion based effects) can be satisfactorily simulated. Following an introduction to the finite element method (initially concentrating on the linear domain), a review is given of the current successes and difficulties associated with the nonlinear modelling of progressive fracturing and the ultimate rupture of RC structures.

## 1.1 FEA: A Simplified Mathematical Explanation

Our understanding and quantification of the fundamental physical processes operating in continua is based to a large extent on our appreciation of the partial differential equations (PDE) describing the variation of the problem variables in space and time. For arbitrary geometries, closed-form solutions for these variations do not exist and one needs to employ a numerical technique to solve the problem. From a mathematical point of view, the finite element method can be seen as an integral solution to PDE. Establishment of the FE integral equations is best done through application of the Galerkin Weighted Residual technique. In the case of stress analysis, the *strong* form of the governing PDE are developed from the notions of force equilibrium (based on the behaviour of an infinitesimal volume), the strain-displacement and stress-strain relationships. For example, static equilibrium in terms of the variation of stresses $\sigma_{ij}$ and body forces $b_i$ may be written as

$$\frac{\partial \sigma_{xx}}{\partial x} + \frac{\partial \sigma_{xy}}{\partial y} + \frac{\partial \sigma_{xz}}{\partial z} + b_x = 0$$

$$\frac{\partial \sigma_{yx}}{\partial x} + \frac{\partial \sigma_{yy}}{\partial y} + \frac{\partial \sigma_{yz}}{\partial z} + b_y = 0$$

$$\frac{\partial \sigma_{zx}}{\partial x} + \frac{\partial \sigma_{zy}}{\partial y} + \frac{\partial \sigma_{zz}}{\partial z} + b_z = 0$$

These differential equations, which hold for every point over the entire solution domain, are transformed into a *weak* integral form by forming the product of each term with an arbitrary *weighting* function and then integrating by parts (Gauss-Green Divergence Theorem).

$$\int_V \frac{\partial u_i}{\partial x_j} \sigma_{ji} dV = \int_S u_i t_i dS + \int_V u_i b_i dV$$

where $u_i$ is the weight function, $t_i$ represents the surface tractions and $S$ and $V$ denote the extent of the surface and volume of the domain in question (repeated subscripts imply tensor contraction). Interpolation of the unknown variables by an approximate *shape* function, operating on discrete *nodal* values of the unknowns, finally yields the FE equations (expressed here in matrix notation)

$$[K]\{d\} + \{f\} = \{r\} \qquad \text{where } [K] = \int_V [B]^T [D][B] dV$$

and the column vectors $\{d\}$, $\{f\}$ and $\{r\}$ are the unknown displacements, the body forces and known applied external loads respectively and [K] is the square structural stiffness matrix. [B] is the partial derivative operator (differentiating the assumed shape functions with respect to the spatial co-ordinates) and [D] the constitutive matrix describing the relationship between stress and strain. The size of the main arrays equals the total number of unknowns in the problem. For many types of analysis, the stiffness matrix is symmetric and sparsely populated with non-zero terms away from the diagonal. This implies that the full matrix need not be stored; an important saving in large analyses.

The manner in which the solution field is assumed to vary (typically approximated by piece-wise polynomial shape functions) is therefore pre-defined and it is only the *best-fit* (in a weighted residual sense) nodal values which need to be found.

The success of the method depends heavily on the availability of a fast, accurate means of solving the system of equations. An efficient numerical integration scheme to form the system matrices is also required as this process is repeated many times during the analysis.

## 1.2. Application of the Mathematical Process

The FE method operates by dividing the surface and interior of the region under consideration into a finite number (a *mesh*) of non-overlapping elements. A pre-defined number of nodal points are associated with each of the elements. Individual nodes may be shared by several elements. Each node has a number of parameters (or degrees of freedom, in a structural mechanics problem) representing the unknowns to be found. The parameters (there may be over 100,000 in a given problem) typically have a clear physical meaning, although this need not necessarily be the case. Table 1 gives a list of typical nodal parameters for common types of analyses.

| Application | Primary Variable | Associated | Secondary |
|---|---|---|---|
| Stress Analysis | Displacement | Force | Stress, Strain |
| | Rotation | Moment | Error estimates |
| Heat Transfer | Temperature | Flux | Interior flux |
| Potential Flow | Potential function | Normal velocity | Interior velocity |
| Navier-Stokes | Velocity | Pressure | Error Estimates |

*Table 1*. FE Nodal Parameters

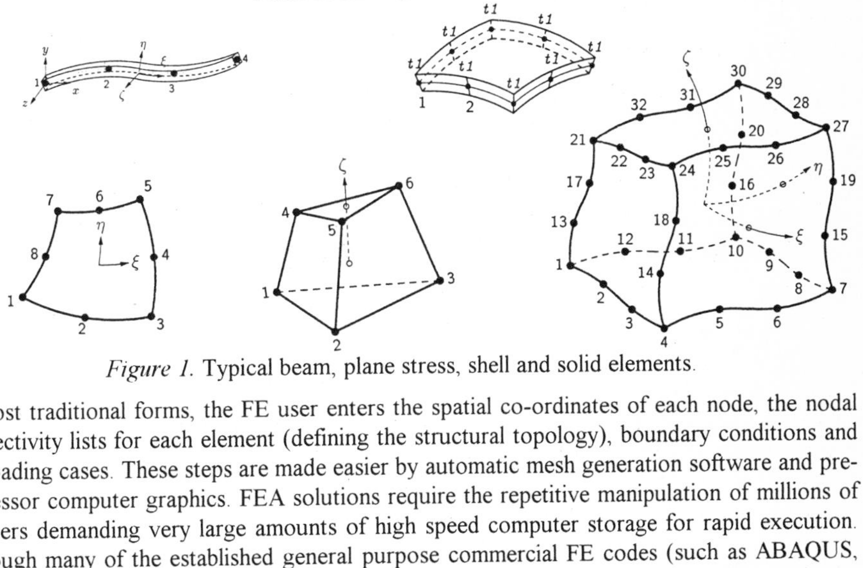

*Figure 1*. Typical beam, plane stress, shell and solid elements.

In most traditional forms, the FE user enters the spatial co-ordinates of each node, the nodal connectivity lists for each element (defining the structural topology), boundary conditions and the loading cases. These steps are made easier by automatic mesh generation software and pre-processor computer graphics. FEA solutions require the repetitive manipulation of millions of numbers demanding very large amounts of high speed computer storage for rapid execution. Although many of the established general purpose commercial FE codes (such as ABAQUS, ADINA, ANSYS, DIANA, LUSAS, NASTRAN and NISA) now have PC versions running on P5/P6+ processors, large scale, sophisticated nonlinear dynamic analyses are best carried out on the latest generation of UNIX based engineering workstations or multi-processor supercomputers.

Users of FE code are spared the task of deriving the element stiffness equations; they may simple select an appropriate element type from a library and declare it during the input stage. For example, the advanced DIANA software currently has 94 element types to choose from, comprising 9 types of truss, 10 beam, 12 plane strain, 7 plane stress, 8 axi-symmetric, 4 plate bending, 8 flat and 7 curved shell, 11 solid, 8 interface, 6 spring, 2 mass and 2 reinforcement elements. Figure 1 illustrates some of these.

## 1.3. Associated Discretisation Techniques

The idea of representing a given domain as a collection of discrete regions is not unique to finite elements but the concept was first applied to aircraft structural analysis where the wings and fuselage were treated as assemblages of stringers, skins and shear panels. In 1941 Hrenikoff introduced the framework method [3], where a plane elastic medium was represented as a collection of truss and beam elements. The use of piece-wise continuous functions defined over a sub-domain to approximate an unknown function can be found in the classic work of Courant [4] who use triangular elements and the principle of minimisation of potential energy to study the St Venant torsion problem. At the time it was treated by most analysts as an idle academic diversion. Practical application of the technique only appeared once digital computers arrived [5]. Other important early contributions include those by Zienkiewicz and Cheung [6] and Clough [7]. By the mid-60s the method really began to take-off. Following 30 years of tremendous growth, FEA now plays a crucial role in the automobile and aerospace industries, and enjoys significant use on the larger construction projects (particularly for the design of tall building and off-shore platforms as well as in bridge and dam engineering).

## 1.4 Reliability of the Method and Its Users

The clear attractions of the method over earlier finite difference approaches lie in its ability to easily handle truly complex boundary geometries and the simplicity with which different materials (including those with anisotropic properties) can be incorporated into the analysis. An immensely important spin-off from the method has been its unifying effect on many branches of engineering and the urgency it created for impressive scientific break-throughs in the areas of material modelling, shell analysis and advanced computer graphics, amongst others.

Questions typically posed by the FE user include[1] (i) Does it matter what kind of elements are adopted and how many should one use? (ii) How much physical detail can be left out? (iii) How accurate will the answers be? (iv) Can the dominant behaviour be modelled as a static or dynamic? (v) Is it essentailly a 2-dimensional, or 3-dimensional process? (vi) How can the actual boundary conditions be represented? To confidently answer these, the user must have a good understanding of how the elements behave and their limitations in order to avoid mis-interpretation or un-realistic expectations. In the hands of an inexperienced engineer, there is always the danger that an FE program will produce an apparently convincing colour plot of stress contours which is at best irrelevant or at worse totally incorrect. All FE solutions are only as good as the mathematical and physical theories they are based on. The assumptions underlying the theories must not be violated and use of FEA is no escape for a poor grasp of applied physics. It is often stated that any analyst unable to perform a simple back-of-the-envelope calculation of the problem, probably does not know enough about it to attempt a solution by FE.

Although the major FE codes are constantly under active development, they have already been shown to be very reliable and effective for many classes of problem. This reliability may be judged on the mathematical rigor of the formulation and their ability to achieve agreement with close form classical solutions and carefully controlled experiments. In the linear domain, proofs

---

[1] For nonlinear problems, the questions are far more taxing. For example (i) Which solution strategy should be used? (ii) What convergence criteria is appropriate? (iii) How can objectivity be assured in strain-softening analyses? (iv) Does the peak load and post-peak response corresponds to the correct equilibrium path?

are available to show that solutions are exact as the mesh density increases[2].

The real power of the method in a structural design, or integrity assessment exercise, is that it allows the user to conduct *numerical experiments* to gain insight into the structural response. These experiments are every bit as valuable (although for different reasons) as those carried out in the laboratory or field. FE results typically provide far more information throughout the structure than is captured in a physical test. They also allow sensitivity analyses to performed, whereby critical parameters are varied within a realistic range and re-runs made at relatively little extra cost.

### 1.5. The Nonlinear Domain: Dynamic Wave Slamming on a RC Caisson

The above description of the FE method focused on solutions in the linear domain. Yet, it is the nonlinear irreversible processes which typically interest engineers working on concrete structures. Three basic sources of non-linearity may be identified for structural problems [8] (i) material non-linearity (as a result of yielding or fracture), (ii) geometric non-linearity (due to changes in the force system brought about by deformation of the structure) and (iii) boundary non-linearity (loss or gain of surface contact). For massive monolithic concrete structures, geometric non-linear effects are negligible. However, this is not the case for slender column or membrane structures. Whilst the source of the non-linearity may differ, the solution approach often follows a common scheme. This paper is concerned mainly with material non-linearity arising from fracturing.

A single non-linear analysis is always more time-consuming than a single linear analysis, not only because multiple steps are required to trace a path-dependent process, but also because a series of iterations invariably need to be carried out within each step. The purpose of these iterations is to reach a state of instantaneous equilibrium within pre-defined tolerances. The process involves iterations not only at the global structural level but also at the local element integration point level.

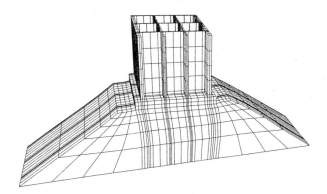

*Figure 2.* Cellular RC Caisson: Deformed FE mesh under Wave Loading.

---

[2] In the nonlinear domain, formal mathematical proofs exist only for a limited class of problems. Nevertheless, impressive agreement between complex nonlinear simulations (even in the difficult field of impact studies) and experimental trials have been found.

Consider the following 3-dimensional stress analysis problem with 25,000 8-noded hexahedral elements and 200,000 unconstrained nodal degrees of freedom (Figure 2). The structure is a cellular RC caisson which forms part of a long harbour wall. The multi-cell box is constructed in a dry-dock, floated out and then towed to its final location. By ballasting with water, the caisson is sunk onto a prepared rubble mound. Once in place, the water inside the cells are displaced by granular fill and a top-slab and sea wall cast in-situ. Conventional design of the front face is based on equivalent static wave loads. The FE study examined the effects of impact loads from storm waves.

Given full Gaussian integration at the element level, 200,000 sampling points need to satisfy local consistency with the constitutive model and global equilibrium has to be met at all the nodal degrees of freedom. In order to trace the deformation response after a moderately slow impact from a breaking wave, an implicit dynamic non-linear analysis was carried out using over five hundred time-steps. (Incorporation of adaptive meshing to better capture the progression of damage would have further slowed down the solution process.) Even with the current rate of advance in computational power, this class of problem required significant CPU time[3]. In addition, the true total CPU time should include the numerous abortive runs which were needed to determine the most appropriate solution strategy.

Once a successful run was completed, additional time was allowed for several sensitivity analyses where mesh definition, material properties and boundary conditions were varied to gain confidence in the solution. Post-processing and interpreting the results can often consume as much run time as the solution phase. Despite the investment required to carry-out such an analysis the technique can offer enormous insight to a problem. For many situations it is effectively the only plausible approach. In the case of the reinforced concrete caisson analysis, many runs were made to examine not only the behaviour under severe wave slamming but also the floating stability and sensitivity of the base slab to unevenness of the foundation bed during placing.

The results enabled important judgements about the structural efficiency of the system to be made, thereby controlling an economic re-design. For example, it was shown that the front wall was excessively over-designed, whereas the base was not. More specifically, the need for divers to prepare the foundation could be rationally decided upon, once tolerances on sea-bed preparation were linked to the ability of the base slab to withstand partial support and some differential settlement. In these preliminary analyses, it was the extent of cracking under typical service loadings which was of most interest, rather than complete collapse state predictions. In fact, as will be discussed subsequently, it is the latter which poses most problems for FE analysts.

## 2. THE NLFE MODELLING OF REINFORCED CONCRETE
### 2.1. The Constitutive Modelling of Concrete: Limitations of Existing Techniques

Considerable effort has been devoted in recent years to understanding and developing constitutive models (that is, nonlinear stress-strain relations) for concrete. Historically, most researchers have tended to treat the compressive behaviour within a different model framework to that used for the tensile response. Whilst this is now changing, it is useful to separate the two regimes for the purpose of this review.

---

[3] A single NLFE analysis took over 32 hours to run on a 200MHz 64-bit R10000 SG INDIGO[2] workstation.

### 2.1.1. Compressive Behaviour

Concrete under compressive stress confinement states can exhibit very significant strength gain, high non-linearity in the stress-strain response and increased ductility when compared to the unconfined uniaxial behaviour. Stiffness degradation and hysteretic damping is also observed under repeated loading.

Whilst there is a universal call for accurate[4], simple models, there has been a tendency amongst the research community to continue to add new features to existing plasticity-based compression models with such relish that they are in danger of collapsing under their own complexity. In certain early cases, the model development phase ended once triaxial test data had been simulated, and not when the model had been incorporated in a numerical scheme and real boundary value problems had been solved.

Despite the large body of constitutive models developed by the research community for the compressive behaviour of concrete, it can be reasonably argued that the vast majority of *nonlinear elasticity* based formulations represent little more than phenomenological curve fits to experimental data, with no attention paid to the role of the constituents. Many of the models employ 10 or more *material constants* which have no physically meaningful link to the internal fabric. Those that claim fewer constants have often been calibrated against a single mix and thus include hidden (fixed) material constants. The use of the uniaxial compressive strength as the primary parameter characterising the multiaxial behaviour of concrete is widespread. This macroscopic treatment has been justified by the assumption that all essential features can be represented without recourse to micro-mechanics. For concrete loaded to its peak nominal stress in compression, the general features include inelastic compaction under hydrostatic loading, shear enhanced compaction, dilation, strain hardening and strain softening.

The theory of plasticity, which is essentially concerned with the dislocation, or *slip*, of the material on the micro-scale, has been used with great success to describe inelastic behaviour of many engineering materials. A number of researchers feel that the mechanical response of concrete exhibits a variety of features which cannot be embraced within the classical theory of plasticity based on conventional stress space formulations. However, the conventional notions of plasticity and fracture are now being re-defined to arrive at a unified approach which covers the full brittle-ductile range of material responses. Continuum damage mechanics (CDM) is an example of a relatively recently developed framework of material description which attempts to cover compressive and tensile regimes with a single approach [9]. CDM models generally employ an energy based criterion to control the evolution of damage. This class of models therefore does not explicitly include stress-based *strength envelopes*. Any strength limits predicted by these formulations are indirect consequences of the governing equations. Current trends also include approaches which combine hardening/softening plasticity formulations with a continuum damage approach to model the degradation in stiffness. An alternative attractive approach is based on the concept of the additive decomposition of slip on multiple planes. This *microplane* model has the strong feature that the evolving anisotropy is captured quite naturally. Like non-associated plasticity models, non-symmetry of the constitutive matrix emerges as slip develops on different planes. This requires greater computational effort when full Newton-Raphson iterations are employed in the nonlinear solution strategy. Both CDM and microplane models are still under development and do not yet feature in mainstream FE software.

---

[4] The accuracy of numerical predictions should lie within the inherent scatter found in carefully conducted experiments.

Unfortunately, the majority of existing commercial FE codes either restrict the user to over-simplified plasticity models in the compression regime (such as Drucker-Prager or Mohr-Coulomb perfect plasticity) with rigorous stress return algorithms, or more sophisticated models with highly dubious stress return strategies. The latter offer little comfort for the FE user and more work is urgently required here. Fortunately, the request for robust plasticity integration schemes is now being answered [10] as material algorithms are appearing which can return consistent and accurate stress increments corresponding to generalised multiaxial strain probes. This is vital since errors in satisfying the plastic consistency condition invariably accumulate, quickly leading to solution locking which has sometimes been falsely interpreted as a signal that the maximum load carrying capacity has been met.

As yet a comprehensive theory for concrete based on rational mechanics principles has not yet appeared in the literature. Perhaps one of the more notable efforts in this direction is the thermodynamic approach advocated by Ortiz and Popov [11]. This formulation explicitly introduces the different mechanical roles of the two dominant phases (aggregate and mortar) into the governing equations and is therefore probably one of the few approaches which justifies the title *constitutive model*. The model includes a simple dependence of the elastic compliances on the extent of microcracking in the mortar. Penny shaped cracks, randomly oriented in the mortar are modelled in an average sense although no crack interaction effects are considered. The process of numerical integration over a finite number of crack directions bears strong resemblance to the technique used in the microplane model [12]. Looking to the future, it is this class of model, which embraces anisotropy in an elegant manner and is able to capture the evolving microstructure, which appears to hold most promise.

Finally, it is now appreciated that greater effort should be made to ensure post-peak stability during softening rather than capturing every feature of the pre-peak compressive behaviour, as it is the former which typically controls the eventual failure mode in concrete structures.

### 2.1.2. Tensile Behaviour

The two established techniques (smeared and discrete) for modelling cracking in concrete have undergone a number of modifications since their original development in the late 1960s [13]. In the case of the discrete crack approach, the intact portion of the concrete structure is generally treated as behaving elastically while crack propagation is simulated by changing the topology of the finite element mesh. The stress singularity at the crack tip drives crack propagation. In the fictitious crack model [14], a fracture process zone (FPZ) is said to exist ahead of the crack tip. In this region, a reduced tensile load can be carried. Crack opening displacement is related to the normal stress by a linear softening model which is controlled by a fixed Fracture Energy Density, $G_f$. Separation of the material either side of the crack may be accomplished in a finite element context by introducing additional nodes and re-meshing the domain locally. An alternative approach is to introduce interface elements at element boundaries at the start of the analysis [15]. In either case, advanced mesh-generators are generally required to model the changing topology. The advances in this area are primarily due to new adaptive meshing procedures.

In a smeared crack approach [16] the behaviour of the fractured concrete is described in terms of a continuum representation. Fracture formation is handled by the strain-softening constitutive relationships. Cracking is assumed to be spatially distributed over the volume (or area in the 2D case) represented by the element's numerical integration point. Rupture surfaces are identified by similarly aligned cracked integration points in adjacent elements. When first introduced [17], this method quickly became popular as it appeared to imply that no change in mesh topology was necessary; thereby suggesting a very efficient computational process. However, during the last decade it has been shown that attempts to model discontinuum processes within a continuum framework (using a strain-softening model) lead to a change in the fundamental characteristics of the governing partial differential equations, rendering them ill-posed [18]. This results in finite element solutions being highly dependent on the mesh density and alignment of the element boundaries[5]. Unlike linear analysis, refinement of a mesh exhibiting continuum strain softening will not produce convergence to the unique, correct solution unless some form of material length scale is introduced into the formulation (see section on localisation, below) or careful adaptive meshing is carried out.

Another major challenge facing fracture investigators at present is the need to establish appropriate criteria for secondary crack formation [19]. Within the family of conventional smeared crack models, two classes exist (i) a fixed crack approach described above and (ii) a rotating crack formulation which follows the major principal stress direction [20]. Recent plane stress comparisons [21] between an *extended* fixed crack model [22] and a rotating crack model, have highlighted the over-stiff behaviour of the former when compared with the latter.

Crisfield and Wills noted that fixed crack models can give solutions with collapse loads that can be significantly too high [23]. Despite these findings, a number of general purpose FE codes still use fixed crack formulations. It has been shown that the extended fixed crack model allows orthogonal cracking in a consistent manner, unlike the standard fixed crack model which can lead to spurious (unbounded) tensile stresses.

Feenstra and de Borst [24] reported on the computational and conceptual problems associated with the decomposition models when cracking is accompanied by plasticity (due to large compressive stresses parallel to the cracks) in one of the sampling points in a FE model. Since tensile loading in one direction leaves the tensile capacity intact in the transverse direction, the evolution of the yield locus by an isotropic hardening/softening rule appears at first insupportable and therefore the use of a kinematic hardening/softening rule has received some study. Despite this, Feenstra and de Borst showed that an isotropically hardening/softening Rankine crack model can provide realistic simulations of crack mouth sliding displacement and overall crack patterns for a mixed-mode fracture experiment.

In cases where significant stress reversals (in addition to rotation of the principal stress directions) can occur, the model should be capable of simulating not only the directional preferences introduced in the material structure but also the de-activation of fractures. For example, consider the situation where a tensile stress state has reached the fracture threshold whereupon (after strain-softening) the stress sense is reversed and compression is now applied to the crack surface. Under these circumstances the crack will close and a large proportion of the *undamaged* compressive stress may be carried across the crack. This feature cannot be modelled by an isotropically softening plasticity model [25] but has been included in a number of multi-directional nonlinear elastic crack models.

## 2.2 Reinforcement Modelling: Continuum and Discrete Approaches

Reinforcement in concrete may either be modelled in a distributed sense by adding directional stiffness to the concrete element or by linking discrete beam or bar elements to the concrete element nodes. In the former approach, some codes (for example ANSYS) distribute the

---

[5] A further consequence of this change in character is that the strain-softened material cannot propagate loading waves.

stiffness over the entire element, whereas others (DIANA) allow bars or membranes to be defined within the element. In either method, perfect bond between the steel and concrete is always implied.

Results from the nonlinear static analysis of a heavily reinforced concrete bridge pier using distributed representation of the steel reinforcement, are now reported. A 5*m* column stub was included in the 3D (half) model of the structure, Figure 3(a). The tapered column head itself was 6.6 by 5.5 by 1.25*m*. The intention was to verify if the sub-structure could safely withstand the design ultimate vertical load of over 14*MN* without excessive yielding of the steel. Fifteen load steps were used to bring the structure up to design service load (the force was applied over three 0.8 by 0.8*m* square patches). A further 20 non-proportional load steps were then used to reach the design ultimate condition. Cracking was initiated at approximately 1.4*MN*. A smeared crack representation was used with a linear strain-softening (constant $G_f$) formulation. An associated Drucker-Prager model was used for the compressive behaviour and a von Mises perfect plasticity model adopted for the reinforcement.

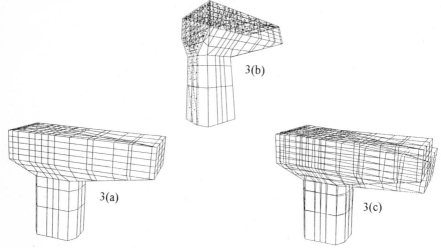

*Figure 3.* Reinforced Concrete Column Head : 3(a) Isometric View of Mesh; 3(b) Isolated Reinforcing Planes and 3(c) Displaced Structure.

As the load was increased to design ultimate, a deep vertical fracture propagated from the top surface of the cross-head down towards the front face of the column, Figures 4(a) and 4(b), as the top of the structure rotated. Significant yielding of one of the minor horizontal bars near the top surface gave rise to increased non-linearity in the load verses end-displacement response. The effects of employing two different forms of strain softening were studied; one with a simple linear decay and the other with a more abrupt loss of strength modelled by a bi-linear decay. The former achieved a higher ultimate load under arc-length control, although both sustained the design loads satisfactorily. The analysis confirmed the expected rupture mode and highlighted the importance of carrying out a sensitivity analysis on the crack model.

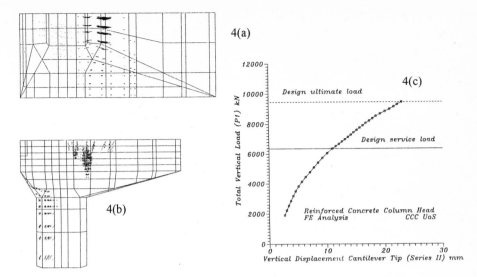

*Figure 4.* Reinforced Concrete Column Head : 4(a), 4(b) Principal Tensile Strains >345με under Design UltimateLoad and 4(c) Load-Displacement Plot.

Returning to the second method of modelling reinforcement; the discrete approach is generally more time-consuming to set-up but it does enable bond-slip and dowel action effects to be incorporated into the analysis. Simple elasto-perfectly plastic (or strain hardening plasticity) models for the reinforcement may be used in both methods. A recent plane stress approach which treats reinforced concrete as a homogenous material [26] has been shown to offer strong simulation capabilities for shear wall and deep beam analyses.

### 2.3. Localisation Issues: The Consequences of Strain-Softening

Perhaps the most formidable challenges faced by the computational mechanics community over the coming years, are those of removing all spurious instabilities in a non-linear finite element analysis and following the correct solution path once bifurcations occur. Lack of equilibrium convergence and loss of stability in the structural stiffness tensor are commonly experienced when undertaking continuum based fracture analyses. Removal of these problems does not automatically infer that a unique, correct solution has been found. Appropriate meshing and material (or element) enrichment when localisation occurs are equally important. Several regularisation procedures which introduce an internal length are under study world-wide. These include *crack-band* methods which adjust the element size with respect to the material model [27] or conversely adjustment of the material parameters with respect to the element size [28]. Other techniques are based on non-local approaches [29], gradient plasticity [30] viscoplastic regularisation [31] and micropolar continua [32]. An alternative method is based on embedding continuum elements with a discontinuity field [33]. The relative merits of each of these have not yet been fully resolved, however both the gradient plasticity and visco-plastic techniques appear to offer real promise.

Two descriptions of continuum failure are currently used. *Diffuse* failure is signalled by the loss of positive definiteness of the symmetric tangential material tensor $^{ep}D^t_{ijkl}$ (at least one eigenvalue of the tensor becomes negative, $det|^{ep}D^t_{ijkl}|<0$); this corresponds to a loss in the second order work [34]. For non-symmetric tangential material tensors (such as found in non-associated plasticity models), the arrival of negative second order work does not generally coincide with a loss of uniqueness. *Localised* failure is synonymous with the discontinuous bifurcation which is signalled by a singularity in the localisation tensor ($det|Q_{jk}|=0$, where $Q_{jk}=n_i{}^{ep}D^t{}_{ijkl}n_l$). Studies have shown that whilst practically all the commonly used continuum elements are able to capture diffuse failure, very few are able to reproduce the localisation condition unless the element boundaries are aligned with the discontinuities [35].

In the case of localised failure, a particular finite element mesh may be incapable of kinematically reproducing a real failure mode. In all but the simplest problems, it is not possible to define an appropriate mesh in advance. For finite element models which lack any form of localisation regularisation, an adaptive meshing scheme is needed whereby the size and alignment of elements is controlled by the solution. The key issue here is choosing the appropriate criteria driving the changes to the mesh. Continual monitoring of the acoustic tensor, or more specifically the direction associated with minimisation of its eigenvalues, offers an attractive new technique to control adaptive meshing and examine the localisation mode. A second issue is that of mapping all solution and state variables from the old to the new mesh. The process is not trivial as the new variables will typically not lead to a converged state without some form of additional iteration loop.

Clearly more work is required in this area before FE collapse load predictions can be made with confidence. The current State-of-the-Art suggests that nonlinear analyses based on continuum concepts are only reliable in commercial FE codes up to the point where weak localisation is initiated. This assumes a $G_f$ approach may be used; if this is not available, nonlinear fracture predictions may in fact be in error the moment the first crack appears. The difficulty of undertaking continuum-based finite element analyses of discontinuum processes is a common theme throughout this paper. One approach to capture the development of a mechanism is based on use of the eigenvectors of the tangent stiffness tensor. The number of unknowns in the model may be drastically reduced by identifying the mode shape associated with a (near) zero eigenvalue and using an indirect displacement control technique on the dominant set of active degrees of freedom [36]. The engineer currently has to look to research codes in order to find techniques which can extend the analysis into these regions where significant rupture occurs. Here, the boundaries between smeared and discrete crack models become blurred. Future FE models will need to be able to make a smooth transition between continuum states and complete break-up if the tool is to realise its full potential.

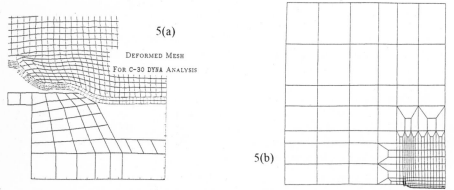

*Figure 5.* Axisymmetric FE Meshs for Reactor Pressure Vessel Wall: 5(a) Deformed DYNA Mesh showing sleeve, inner tube and concrete near impact site; 5(b) Crack Pattern from Implicit Analysis following Impact.

Figure 5(a) shows a portion of an axi-symmetric mesh used to model a reactor pressure vessel aperture. A series of initial analyses were performed using the explicit dynamic code DYNA to determine likely envelopes for the force-time histories following impact of a steel tube with the lining of the circular aperture. The impact site was at the point where the penetration reduces in diameter.

The impact force-time signatures were used as the forcing functions for a subsequent series of implicit dynamic analyses. The logic for this two-stage approach was that the explicit code had a less than satisfactory fracture model for concrete, whereas the implicit code had no capability to model impact events. The purpose of this analysis was to examine the possibility of a shear plug being ejected from the wall of the vessel following high velocity impact from the 4500*kg* tube. Automatic re-meshing was used as quadrilateral elements became distorted in the DYNA runs (Figure 5(b)). Contact boundaries were defined on both the tube and aperture sleeve. Over 50 nonlinear analyses were performed to gain confidence in the results and explore the sensitivity of the shape of the impulse on the second phase analysis results. Whilst significant radial cracking was predicted local to the impact site (Figure 5(b)), none of the runs suggested the fractures would be driven to the outer face.

### 2.4. The Nonlinear Solution Algorithm

Identification of the ultimate rupture mechanism in a reinforced concrete structure is of utmost importance to the structural engineer. For many structural forms and load conditions, the collapse mode is self-evident. For complex structures under multiple load cases, it is not so clear. This is where nonlinear FE analysis has the potential to provide the missing insight. However, currently no single incremental-iterative solution strategy can guarantee that a particular FE analysis will follow the correct solution path. For example, experience has shown that the simple modified Newton-Raphson iterative procedure can sometimes converge in a stable manner whereas full Newton-Raphson does not. Yet the former might trace an unstable equilibrium path, beyond crack initiation in the case of multiple bifurcations. Whilst some form of spherical or up-dated normal arc-length [37] incremental method combined with a line-search procedure is most likely to succeed, the choice of convergence criterion for the iterative process is not clear. Restricting minimisation of the residuals to the degrees of freedom locally associated with crack opening (rather than all degrees of freedom throughout the structure) has been shown to be successful in certain cases. The commercial FE code developers generally offer little advice here, often because they themselves are unclear. More research is desperately required to clearly identify why a premature lack of convergence occurs. These problems are undoubtedly linked to the stability of the plasticity integration algorithm and degree of stress re-distribution likely in a highly kinematically redundant strain-softening RC structure.

### 3. DURABILITY ASPECTS: MODELLING ELECTRO-CHEMICAL PHENOMENA IN CONJUNCTION WITH THERMO-MECHANICAL PROCESSES

Finite element analysis has been routinely used for diffusion studies in the field of geomechanical seepage analysis and heat transfer. The governing steady state quasi-harmonic equation is also encountered in many other fields, including the distribution of magnetic and electric flux and chemical concentration. The processes of moisture loss during hydration, chloride migration and thermal conduction through concrete are governed by similar equations.

In order to undertake a detailed concrete durability study where long term process dominate, each of the time-dependent phenomena (for example, creep, shrinkage, heat of hydration, stiffness evolution, thermal expansion, moisture transport, chemical alteration under thermal transients, progressive micro-cracking, chloride penetration, carbonation and corrosion of steel reinforcement) could be incorporated in a coupled, multi-physics analysis. In principle, much of this is already possible [38] yet the application of FEA to this field is still in its infancy.

As an example of the complex interaction between environmental conditions, consider the mechanism of chloride penetration which involves a diffusion process and the chemical binding of chloride ions with the hydration products of concrete. In order to estimate the rate of corrosion, an analysis must link the chloride concentration to the rate of oxygen diffusion to the cathode, the resistivity of the pore solution and the temperature of the substrate. The rate of corrosion should in turn be related to the mechanical loss of bond and spalling of cover concrete to finally allow realistic residual strength assessments to be made. Once cracks form, the boundary conditions change and hence the rate of chloride penetration will alter. This suggests a highly nonlinear process where a FE mixed formulation is required to handle the different variables. The structural engineer needs to assess how sensitive the load-carrying capacity and deformation modes are to this potential local loss of bond[6]. Equally importantly, the engineer needs to estimate the optimum time to carry out any repairs from the viewpoints of safety and economy.

Anchorage and bond fatigue behaviour in deformed bars involve relatively complex local phenomena which do not lead themselves to be easily or efficiently incorporated in a NLFE analysis. Further research is required here to develop robust macroscopic models for these mechanisms [39]. Despite these complications, FEA can already greatly assist the engineer in deciding whether loss of steel area or concrete section will significantly affect the overall integrity of a complex structure. For example, assuming no significant slip occurs in well anchored deformed reinforcing bars, the ability to locally modify the material properties, percentage of steel reinforcement and change the boundary conditions or loading system in a FE analysis allows sensitivity analyses to be performed relatively easily.

## 4. FUTURE EXPECTATIONS OF NONLINEAR COMPUTATIONAL MECHANICS

The future for FEA (and its successors) expanding into new areas of analysis looks assured. Continued growth in the nonlinear domain requires that ever more efficient, stable nonlinear solution strategies be found and refined shell/brick/interface elements be developed. On the development of constitutive models, much closer links between micro-structural processes and the macroscopic response is required. This will require a new generation of high precision experimental rigs to supply fundamental material data. Smooth transitions between continuum and discontinuum modelling (through localisation indicators, adaptive constitutive modelling and automatic mesh refinement) are urgently needed to realistically simulate the complete collapse and disintegration of 3D structures. Over the coming years, meshless methods [40] are likely to gain popularity and cloning techniques [41] be used to simulate far-field conditions. A greater understanding of the coupling between thermo-mechanical and electro-chemical processes is also necessary before FEA becomes a routine tool in durability studies.

Widespread use of notebook and desktop personal machines which can easily access massive clusters of similar computers and parallel supercomputers will enable true, large scale multi-physics simulations to be made and probabilistic based studies to be performed. Web-based libraries of elements, constitutive models, FE subroutines, benchmark problems and

---

[6] A recent BRITE/EURAM project *The Service Life of Reinforced Concrete Structures* (BE-4062) has addressed some of these issues.

fundamental experimental data should be established. Optimum material selection and modelling will be automated in the large generic FE codes.

The clear trends in reduced computing costs suggest that the original approach of creating several different meshes for different types of analyses on the same structure (in order to reduce the computational burden at run time) may be replaced in the future by definition of a single, more detailed but less efficient, model which can be used repeatedly. Pre and Post-Processing visualisation techniques will be enhanced, taking advantage of large screen, high resolution, textured animations using multiple transparent iso-surfaces and tensor maps combined with 3D audio effects. Real advances in our understanding of how large civil engineering structures behave will follow once more structures have arrays of sensors permanently embedded during construction. Remote monitoring of this data will be used to continually refine FE models.

FEA is simply a powerful tool which enables us to model our surroundings. It will continue to do so with even greater realism, offering the prospect for safer, more economic and also more creative engineering structures.

## REFERENCES

1. *Finite Element Analysis of Reinforced Concrete Structures II*, Isenberg, J (*Ed.*), ASCE, **1993**, *717*. *RC Elements under Cyclic Load*, (originally published as CEB 210) Comite euro-international du beton, **1996**, *190*.
2. Smith, P C, Owen, D R J and Bicanic, N, *A Theoretical and Practical Study of the Use of Non-Linear Finite Element Codes to Analyse Concrete Vessels and Containments*, HSE Research & Development Report R9, **1996**, *193*.
3. Hrenikoff, A, Solution to problems in elasticity by the framework method, *J Applied Mech.*, A8, **1941**, *169-175*.
4. Courant, R, Variational methods for the solution of problems of equilibrium and vibration, *Bull. American Math. Soc.*, 49, **1943**, *1-23*.
5. Turner, M J, Clough, R W, Martin, H C and Topp, L J, Stiffness and deflection analysis of complex structures, *J Aero. Sci.*, 23, **1956**, *805-823*. Argyris, J H, Energy theorems and structural analysis, Butterworth, 1960 (reprinted from *Aircraft Eng.*, **1954**.)
6. Zienkiewicz, O C and Cheung, Y K, Buttress dams on complex rock foundations, *Water Power*, 16, **1964**, *193*.
7. Clough, R W, The finite element method in plane stress analysis, *Proc. 2nd ASCE Conf. Electronic Computation*, **1960**.
8. *NAFEMS Introduction to Nonlinear Finite Element Analysis*, Hinton, E (*Ed.*), NAFEMS, **1992**, *380*.
9. Kachanov, M, Continuum model of medium with cracks, *J Eng Mech*, ASCE, 106(5), **1980**, *1039-1051*.
10. Simo, J C and Taylor, R L, A return mapping algorithm for plane stress elasto-plasticity, *Int J Num. Meth. Engng.*, 22, **1986**, *649-670*. Pearce, C J and Bicanic, N, On Multi-surface plasticity and Rankine Model, *5th Int Conf. Computational Plasticity: Fundamentals and Applications*, Owen, Oñate and Hinton (*Eds.*), **1997**, *957-964*.
11. Ortiz, M and Popov, E P, A physical model for the inelasticity of concrete, *Proc R Soc Lond*, A 383 **1982**, *101-125*.
12. Carol, I, Prat, P and Bazant, Z P, New explicit microplane model for concrete: Theoretical aspects and numerical implementation, *Int J Solids and Structures*, 29(9), **1992**, *1173-1191*. Qiu, Y and Crouch, R S, Spurious compaction in the microplane model and a new adaptive

framework, $5^{th}$ *Int Conf. Computational Plasticity: Fundamentals and Applications*, Owen, Oñate and Hinton (*Eds.*), **1997**, *493-499*. Qiu, Y and Crouch, R S, Optimisation and sensitivity of the material constants in the microplane model, $5^{th}$ *Int Conf. Computational Plasticity: Fundamentals and Applications*, Owen, Oñate and Hinton (*Eds.*), **1997**, *500-506*.

13. Ngo, D and Scordelis, A C, Finite element analysis of reinforced concrete beams, *J Amer. Concrete Institute*, 64(14), **1967**, *152-163*. Nilson, A, Nonlinear analysis of reinforced concrete by the finite element method, *J Amer. Concrete Institute*, 65(9), **1968**, *757-766*.

14. Hillerborg, Modéer, M and Petersson, P, Analysis of crack formation and crack growth in concrete by means of fracture mechanics and finite elements, *Cement and Concrete Research*, 6(6), **1976**, *773-781*.

15. Rots, J, Computational modelling of concrete fracture, PhD Thesis, University of Delft, **1988**. Vonk, R, Softening of concrete loaded in compression, PhD Thesis, University of Eindhoven, **1992**.

16. Rashid, Y R, Analysis of pre-stressed concrete pressure vessels, *Nuclear Engineering Design*, 7(44), **1968**, *334-355*.

17. Cervenka, V, Inelastic finite element analysis of reinforced concrete panels under in-plane loads, PhD Thesis, University of Colorado, **1970**. Suidan, M and Schnobrich, W, Finite element analysis of reinforced concrete, *ASCE J Structures Division*, 99(10), **1973**, *2109-2122*.

18. Slys, L J, Wave propagation, localization and dispersion in softening solids, PhD Thesis, University of Delft, **1992**.

19. *Fracture Mechanics of Concrete: Concepts, Models and Determination of Material Properties*, Report by ACI Committee 446, Bazant, Z P (Chairman), **1989**.

20. Cope, R J, Rao, P V, Clarke, L A and Norris, P, Modelling of reinforced concrete behaviour for finite element analysis of bridge slabs, in Taylor, Hinton and Owen (*Eds.*), *Numerical methods for non-linear problems*, Pineridge Press, Swansea, **1980**, *457-470*.

21. Guzina, B B, Rizzi, E, Willam, K and Pak, R Y S, Failure prediction of smeared-crack formulations, *ASCE J Eng Mech*, 121(1), **1995**, *150-161*.

22. Rots, J G and Blaauwendraad, J, *Crack models for concrete: Discrete or smeared? Fixed, multidirectional or rotating?*, Heron, 34(1), **1989**.

23. Crisfield, M A and Wills, J, Numerical Comparisons Involving Different Concrete-Models, *IABSE Colloquium on Computational Mechanics of Concrete Structures - Advances and Applications*, Delft, IABSE Report Volume 54, **1987**, *177-187*.

24. Feenstra, P H and de Borst, R, A plasticity model and algorithm for Mode-I cracking in concrete, *Int J Num Meth Eng.*, 38, **1995**, *2509-2529*.

25. Hansen, N R and Schreyer, H L, Deactivation of damage effects, *Recent advances in damage mechanics and plasticity*, AMD 132 : MD 30, ASME, **1992**, *63-76*.

26. Feenstra, P H and de Borst, R, *Aspects of Robust Computational Modeling for Plain and Reinforced Concrete*, Heron 38(4), **1993**, *76*.

27. Bazant, Z P and Oh, D Crack band theory for fracture of concrete, *Materials & Structures*, 16(93), **1983**, *155-177*.

28. Pietruszczak, S and Mroz, Z, Finite element analysis of deformation of strain-softening materials, *Int J Num. Meth. in Eng.*, 17, **1981**, *327-334*. Willam, K, Experimental and computational aspects of concrete fracture, *Computer-aided analysis and design of concrete structures*, Damjanic, Hinton, Owen, Bicanic and Simovic (*Eds.*), Pineridge Press, **1984**, *33-70*.

29. Bazant, Z P and Pijaudier-Cabot, G, Non-local continuum damage, localisation stability and convergence, *J Applied Mech.*, 55(2), *287-293*.

30. Vardoulakis, I and Aifantis, E, A gradient flow theory of plasticity for granular materials, *Acta Mechanica*, 87, **1991**, *197-217*.

31. Neddleman, Material rate dependence and mesh sensitivity on localisation problems, *Comp. Meth. Applied Mech. Eng.*, 67, **1988**, *69-86*.

32. Steinmann, M and Willam, K, Performance of enhanced finite element formulations in localised failure computations, *Comp. Meth. in Appl. and Mech. Eng.*, 90, **1991**, *845-867*.

33. Simo, J, Oliver, J and Armero, F, An analysis of strong discontinuities induced by strain softening in rate-independent inelastic solids, *Computational Mech.*, 12, **1993**, *277-296*.

34. Hill, R, A General Theory of Uniqueness and Stability in Elastic-Plastic Solids, *Mechanics & Physics of Solids*, 6, **1958**, *236-249*.

35. Steinmann, P and Willam, K, Finite Elements for Capturing Localized Failure, *Archive of Applied Mechanics*, Springer-Verlag, 61, **1991**, *259-275*.

36. Napoleao, J, Elwi, A E and Murray, D W, *An Eigenvector-Based Strategy for Analysis of Inelastic Structures*, Structural Engineering Report 166, Department of Civil Engineering, University of Alberta, **1990**.

37. Crisfield, M A, *Nonlinear finite element analysis of solids and structures*, Volume 1, J Wiley & Sons, **1994**.

38. Bazant, Z P, Nonstationary Long-Term Processes Causing Loss of Serviceability, *IABSE Colloquium on Computational Mechanics of Concrete Structures - Advances and Applications*, Delft, IABSE Report Volume 54, **1987**, *261-284*.

39. Rodriguez, J, Ortega, L M and Garcia, A M, Assessment of Structural Elements with Corroded Reinforcement, *Corrosion and Corrosion Protection of Steel in Concrete*, Swamy, (*Ed.*), Sheffield Academic Press, 1, **1994**, *171-185*.

40. Belytschko, T, Lu, Y and Gu, L, Element free Galerkin methods, *Int J Num Meth Engng.*, 37, **1994**, *229-256*.

41. Wolf, J P and Song, C, Consistent infinitesimal finite-element cell method: In-plane motion, *Computer Meth. Applied Mech. & Eng.*, 123, **1995**, *355-370*.

# The Inspection and Evaluation of Nuclear Related Civil Engineering Structures

JOHN P McFARLANE  CEng MICE MIMechE MINucE FIES,  DR LESLEY M SMITH
PhD CEng MICE MIStructE MINucE FGS AND COLIN BAIRD   CEng MICE MINucE
Scottish Nuclear Limited, UK

## SYNOPSIS

Nuclear Safety Related Civil Structures are the subject of an ongoing Inspection and Evaluation programme as set out in the Site Licence Conditions for each Nuclear Power Plant Site.

This paper describes the different classes of structure encountered on Nuclear Power Plants and the procedures that are used during their inspection and evaluation.  Structural inspection is carried out by periodic surveys and may include continuous or quasi-continuous condition monitoring depending on the type and importance of each structure.

The paper describes the methods employed in the evaluation of structures plus the use of engineering judgement and fixed acceptance criteria to confirm their continued fitness for purpose. This is based on consideration of original design criteria, external hazards, and any subsequent changes in loading conditions and design codes.

Historical records and databases and comparison with the performance of similar structures are used to identify the effects of ageing and any identified trending. Inspection and monitoring activities on the Nuclear Power Plants operated by Nuclear Electric and Scottish Nuclear over the last 25 years have allowed a pattern of behaviour to be established and the results of Periodic Safety Reviews have demonstrated that the Civil Engineering Structures are performing in accordance with the design intent.

This Paper sets out the strategy adopted by the British Energy Group in its approach to ensuring ongoing fitness for purpose by continued surveillance,  materials testing,  review of historical data,  ongoing research through the Industry's Technical Working Groups and development of modern analytical techniques.

## INTRODUCTION

Scottish Nuclear (SN) and Nuclear Electric (NEL), subsidiaries of British Energy (BE), own and operate seven Advanced Gas-cooled Reactor (AGR) nuclear power stations at Torness, Hunterston B, Heysham 1 and 2, Hartlepool, Dungeness B, and Hinkley Point B and a Pressurised Water Reactor (PWR) at Sizewell B.

*Management of concrete structures for long-term serviceability.* Thomas Telford, London, 1997

A variety of civil engineering structures and associated plant is present on the nuclear power stations. These structures are valuable assets which need to be maintained to ensure that they continue to perform their function to protect the plant and maintain nuclear safety. In-service inspection and monitoring are carried out on civil structures at nuclear power stations to ensure that nuclear safety is maintained and that the structures are in a serviceable condition to allow continued generation and commercial operation.

Nuclear safety related structures comprise those structures which fulfil a function that is necessary to maintain or guarantee nuclear safety. This can be an active role whereby a structure must actively support or protect a service or item of plant which is essential, or a passive role in which case a structure under accidental loading or fault conditions must not fail in a manner such that an essential service or item of plant is compromised.

SN and NEL carry out documented periodic structural inspections of all of the nuclear safety related structures and buildings in accordance with the Nuclear Site Licence conditions. The reactors are contained within prestressed concrete pressure vessels (PCPV) or prestressed concrete containment vessel (PCCV) which are subject to specific procedures for monitoring and maintenance [ 1 & 2 ] and a complementary series of procedures are used for the inspection of other nuclear safety related structures.

Other, non nuclear safety related, structures such as administration buildings and workshops are subject to a less formal or ad hoc regime of inspection and maintenance. In common with many other industries it is important that various facilities are maintained for safety reasons and to prevent potential economic and commercial loss should they not be available.

This Paper sets out the strategy adopted by the British Energy Group in its approach to ensuring ongoing fitness for purpose by continued surveillance, materials testing, review of historical data, ongoing research through the Industry's Technical Working Groups and development of modern analytical techniques.

## STATUTORY REQUIREMENTS

Each site is covered by a nuclear site licence which is issued to the operator under the provisions of the Nuclear Installations Act 1965 (and subsequent amendments)[ 3 ] by HM Nuclear Installations Inspectorate (NII) which is part of the Nuclear Safety Division of the UK Health and Safety Executive (HSE). The licence currently contains 35 standard conditions which must be met by the operator by means of established and approved compliance arrangements. However, the rules are not prescriptive and the licensee retains absolute responsibility for nuclear safety under UK law. It is the duty of the NII to; ensure that the appropriate standards are developed, achieved and maintained by the licensee; ensure that the necessary safety precautions are taken; and monitor and regulate the safety of the plant by means of its powers under the licence and relevant regulations [ 4 ].

The regulatory requirements have major implications for the in-service inspection regime, principally through site licence condition 28, which covers the examination, inspection, maintenance and testing of all plant and structures that may affect nuclear safety. A safety case containing the relevant information with regard to design and operational parameters and limits is produced by the licensee in accordance with arrangements approved by the NII. It is essential that all structures must be maintained throughout their operational life in such a way that they are always fit for purpose and capable of meeting their nuclear safety role as required by the safety case which is identified in the licence conditions. In order to do this they must be examined, inspected and tested in a manner and at a frequency which is adequate to confirm that the structural integrity, performance and reliability claims made in the safety case continue to be met throughout the operational life of the station.

There are three basic classes of structures which are monitored under the statutory requirements:

- Prestressed Concrete Pressure Vessels (Structures, enclosing a nuclear reactor, that contain the pressurised primary coolant during the operation of the plant)
- Prestressed Concrete Containment Vessels (Structures, enclosing a nuclear reactor and its pressure vessel, that provide containment in the event of a failure in the system)
- Other nuclear safety related structures

This paper will concentrate on the in-service monitoring and inspection of the three classes of structures covered by the statutory requirements.

As well as the specific requirements of the Nuclear Site Licence, the Stations are covered by other legislation that would affect any other large industrial plant. With regard to structural inspection requirements, however, the provisions of the Pressurised Systems & Transportable Gas Containers Regulations 1989 ([ 5 ] ) as they affect the PCPVs are of particular note. The Operating Company (SN/NEL) is the Competent Person referred to in the regulations with the Appointed Examiner for the PCPVs being the Competent Individual referred to in the regulations and identified as a suitably qualified and experienced person (SQEP) to carry out and supervise inspections. The Appointed Examiner's report which is submitted under the Nuclear Site Licence conditions meets the reporting requirements of Regulation 9.

## DESIGN APPROACH
### Prestressed Concrete Pressure Vessel Design
In most cases the PCPVs contain the nuclear reactor and the boilers used to produce steam in order to generate electricity in a single central cavity or vault. In the case of Heysham I and Hartlepool the boilers are housed in individual cylindrical cavities within the thickness of the vessel wall and the reactor is contained in the main vault of the vessel. The principal structural functions of the vessels are:

- To provide primary containment to the reactor and to prevent the uncontrolled release to the environment of fission products.
- To provide and maintain radiological shielding.
- To support the reactor and boilers
- To provide support to the steel PCPV liner and penetration liners thus creating the pressure enclosure for the carbon dioxide gas circuit which transports heat from the reactor core to the boilers.
- To protect plant and equipment from external events.

A steel liner on the inside of the concrete pressure vessel, together with the penetration liners, provides a gas-tight membrane, retaining the reactor coolant. The liner, which is anchored to the PCPV concrete, contributes to reactor coolant gas leak prevention but does not contribute to the load resisting capacity of the PCPV. Therefore the PCPV's ultimate strength does not rely on the presence of either an intact or leaking liner. The temperature of this liner, and that of the surrounding concrete, is maintained within design limits by internal insulation and by circulation of cooling water through pipes welded to the liner and embedded in the concrete.

Although the PCPV's were designed some years ago to Codes of Practice and British Standards now considered superseded, the general approach taken was to ensure large factors of safety against ultimate failure load. This allowed for a margin which envelopes the effects of transient loadings, local discontinuities and material variation and the limits of the structural analysis tools available at that time to be catered for in the design. Examples of the design codes in force at the time of the design of the early vessels were, CP 114 The Structural Use of Reinforced Concrete in Buildings [ 6 ] and CP 115 The Structural Use of Prestressed Concrete in Buildings [ 7 ]. These codes are essentially load-factor design documents in which permissible working stresses are defined as a proportion of the material strength. The analysis to consider ultimate loads and to demonstrate an adequate margin over working loads was supplemented by scale model testing and predicted modes of failure were checked. A design pressure of 1.1 x Operating Pressure was adopted and a Proof Pressure Test (PPT) was also carried out at 1.15 x Design Pressure (i.e. 1.265 x Operating Pressure) before the vessels were commissioned for service. The displacements obtained from this test were used to demonstrate linear behaviour, and, in some case to calibrate finite element models subsequently produced.

More recent codes (CP110, 1972 [ 8 ] leading, in 1985, to BS 8110 [ 9 ]), introduced the limit state design concept, in which the probability of the structure performing satisfactorily during its design life is assessed both in terms of the ultimate and serviceability limit states (i.e. failure and various in-service conditions) which take into account durability and long term performance aspects. Partial safety factors are defined for loads and materials properties. These factors take into account variability and the importance of the limit state being considered.

In fact, the importance of concrete mix specification and durability aspects was recognised at the time of the design of the early vessels, and the design basis significantly exceeded the minimum requirements of CP 114 and CP 115. The procedures used and experience gained with the design of the early vessels for both Magnox and AGR stations were incorporated into a new British Standard, BS 4975, issued in 1973 [ 10 ], which specifically addressed PCPVs for nuclear reactors. This standard was prepared as a digest of experience to date and as such reflected, in large measure, the approach which had already been adopted in the design of the vessels from first principles. The standard retained the load factor design concept of CP 114 and CP 115, whilst including aspects such as serviceability, quality control and in-service surveillance. BS 4975 was re-issued in 1990 [ 11 ] with a number of amendments and additions, reflecting the experience gained in the intervening period, and including additional appendices providing guidance on assessment methods and documentation requirements. In common with other current UK design codes, BS 4975 now specifies material properties in terms of characteristic rather than guaranteed values. (The characteristic strength is the strength at which only 5% of samples are expected to fail).

The overall structural integrity of the PCPV is provided by the joint action of the structural concrete forming the vessel and the prestressing system (which maintains the PCPV structure under compression during normal operation and under fault conditions); no contribution to the overall structural strength is assumed to be provided by the steel liner.

The basic requirement for vessel integrity is the retention of the concrete in an overall compressive state. Potential vessel failure modes therefore mostly relate to over pressurisation, loss of prestress or deterioration of the stressing system or local stressing caused, for example, by thermal effects. Possible modes of failure and the design or operational features provided to protect against them are summarised overleaf.

The nature of the PCPV construction confers a high tolerance to defects. The prestressing tendons are mechanically independent making simultaneous failure extremely unlikely. Failure of any one tendon would have an insignificant effect on the overall vessel stress state. In addition, whereas in a steel vessel, the appearance of a small defect causes large local stress concentrations at the crack front, a crack in concrete does not generally result in large stress concentrations because, due to the composite aggregate nature of the material, a large zone of dispersed microcracks is formed at the crack front. This microcracking effectively blunts the stress concentration. Thus concrete is a material of low sensitivity to flaws. This tendency towards distributed microcracking together with the stress/strain characteristic of prestressing steel, confers on a PCPV a large amount of ductility, i.e. the deformation at failure is much greater than that under service loads. Such a failure would occur gradually and with the absorption of a large amount of energy.

| | |
|---|---|
| Over-pressurisation | Large (> 2.5 times) margin between operational pressures and ultimate failure load. High reliability of safety relief valve and pressure monitoring systems |
| Reduction in tendon load | Regular monitoring with opportunity to adjust prestress level if necessary. Compressive strains and elastic behaviour confirmed by strain gauges and vessel deflection measurements |
| Tendon / anchorage damage or corrosion | Regular monitoring via Maintenance Schedule inspections. Opportunity for replacement of unbonded tendons if necessary |
| Overheating of vessel | Two independent vessel cooling circuits with extensive concrete temperature measurements and regular checks of cooling circuit performance and temperatures . High thermal capacity of concrete. |
| High differential temperatures in top slab | Individual control on cooling water flow to standpipes. Operating Rule limitation on temperature differentials. |
| Hot gas impingement on tendons | High liner integrity. High tendon redundancy and independence of individual tendons. $CO_2$ likely to vent through relatively few tendon ducts thus minimising damage to prestressing system. Leakage monitoring. |

It is important to note that the design of the PCPVs was carried out on the basis of a large margin (>2.5) between operational pressure loads and the ultimate failure load and that, from the outset, consideration was given to through life structural monitoring, although this was not specifically included in BS 4975 until the 1990 edition.

Although not specifically included in some of the early designs, hazard loadings such as seismic, missiles, high winds, extreme ambient temperatures etc. have to be considered. Due to the heavy construction of the PCPVs, substantial margins are available to resist these infrequent loads. The Periodic Safety Reviews carried out under the site licence provide for a detailed assessment of internal and external hazards.

## Prestressed Concrete Containment Vessel Design

For the PCCV at Sizewell B, Bechtel's generic design was adopted as the UK [ ?? ] design and, after an extensive review, modified American design codes were established. The PCCV, both concrete and liner, were designed in accordance with the *Design and Construction Rules for PWR Primary Containment* derived from a modified ASME III Division 2 Subsection CC [ 12 ]. The UK PWR containment design code definitions are more in line with BS 4975, design allowables are expressed in UK terms of 28 day concrete cube strength and reinforcement yield strength for UK steel, and again in line with BS 4975 there is an additional requirement to check the ultimate capacity of the containment to withstand an internal pressure loading at ambient temperature to demonstrate an ultimate minimum safety factor of 2.0 (cf. 2.5 for PCPVs).

The PCCV primary containment structure is required to perform the following functions:

- To house and support enclosed plant in a suitable environment in combination with the heating, ventilation and air-conditioning system.
- To provide support to the secondary containment dome.
- To protect plant and equipment from external events.
- To provide and maintain radiological shielding.
- In conjunction with the primary containment liner and other systems, to prevent the uncontrolled release to the environment of fission products.
- To withstand the effects of normal and exceptional load combinations in order to ensure the structure does not prevent adjacent structures from functioning as required.

The design of the containment is based on a number of specified load combinations which are divided into the categories of construction, normal, exceptional and ultimate. With the exception of the Structural Overpressure Test (SOT) and Integrated Leak Rate Test (ILRT) combinations, the containment experiences only minor internal pressure loading under Normal Operating Conditions (NOC). Under exceptional conditions significant internal pressure loadings can be generated during the specified faults. The peak pressure from the pressure time transients associated with these faults is deemed to be the design basis fault pressure. Linear elastic behaviour of the containment shell is ensured by designing the prestressing system to maintain net compression in the cylindrical wall and hemispherical dome under all normal operating conditions, including the test conditions [ 13 ].

| Category | Design Internal Pressure | Design Philosophy |
|---|---|---|
| Normal (SOT) | 1.15P | Linear elastic behaviour |
| Normal (ILRT) | 1.00P | |
| Exceptional | 1.50P | Essentially linear elastic behaviour but with local areas beyond this limit. |
| | 1.00P* | |
| Ultimate | >2.00P | Elastic/plastic behaviour with materials at characteristic strengths. |

*In association with seismic loading                    P= 50 psig (0.345MPa)

Substantial margins are available because of the onerous combination of fault loadings used e.g. the maximum safe shutdown earthquake (SSE) of 0.25g peak horizontal freefield acceleration combined with the maximum loss of coolant accident (LOCA) pressure loading.

### Design of Nuclear Safety Related Structures

The design codes and standards that were used in the design of other safety related structures have, like those used in the design of the PCPVs, developed through time. In addition to the changes to the concrete codes outlined above, there have been major changes to the structural steel, load bearing brickwork, and loading codes reflecting the general move towards limit state design. Consequently modifications to structures are likely to have been to different codes from those used in the original design.

The nuclear safety related structures at Sizewell were designed in accordance with a design code derived from ACI 349 [ 14 ] together with, for some structures, additional sections taken from ACI 318 provisions [ 15 ], with modifications in respect of UK materials, workmanship practices and allowable design parameters.

## MATERIALS
### PCPV Materials - Concrete

The pressure vessels were cast on site from high strength concrete, using a blend of Ordinary Portland Cement (OPC) with, in some cases, Pulverised Fuel Ash (PFA) or Ground Granulated Blast Furnace Slag Cement (GGBFS) as a cement replacement, and locally sourced aggregates (see Table 4). In some vessels the anchorage blocks for the prestressing system were cast separately using a mix with a higher specified minimum strength than the main pressure vessel in order to withstand the high local stresses. In most mixes a plasticiser was specified for the main vessel mix to assist concrete flow around tendon ducts and embedded steel and to aid compaction. High workability mixes were required for the congested top cap standpipe zones of the PCPVs . Details of the various material properties for the concretes used in the construction of the PCPVs for Magnox and AGR stations are given in [ 16 ] which also includes consideration of ageing and durability issues and non-operational thermal loading. This information is based on the station case histories (construction records), long term testing, research and studies on material ageing and is used as source material during structural assessment.

### PCPV Materials - Prestressing System

A variety of different types of prestressing systems is used on the PCPVs. However it should be noted that, unlike most other civil structures, all the systems used on PCPVs employ un-grouted tendons to allow withdrawal and in-service inspection and re-stressing of tendons should this be required. Corrosion protection of the un-grouted tendons is provided by various treatments applied to the prestressing wire, strand, tendons and ducts. Generally a factory applied corrosion protection system on the wire or strand is augmented by the application of a suitable grease during installation of the tendons. This method of protection has performed well in service with tests confirming that effective protection is still provided after 20 years operation.

### PCCV Materials - Concrete

Four main classes of concrete were used at Sizewell B [30]:

- C5 - A mass fill concrete incorporating 50% PFA
  (characteristic strength 10 N/mm2)

- C1 - A structural concrete incorporating 40% PFA
  (characteristic strength 45 N/mm2)
- C2 - A structural concrete incorporating 40% PFA
  (characteristic strength 30 N/mm2)
- C11LW - A lightweight concrete incorporating sintered PFA lightweight
  aggregate (characteristic strength 45 N/mm2)

The C5 mix was used beneath the foundations of higher structures where buildings with differing foundation levels were constructed adjacent to each other. Class C1 concrete was used in the primary containment and the internal structures of the reactor building. Concrete of class C2 was used in the construction of the other power station buildings and the lightweight concrete class C11LW was used for the secondary containment dome. Details of the various material properties for the concretes used in the construction of the PCCV for Sizewell B are retained in the station lifetime records. It is intended that details of the Sizewell B PCCV concrete will be included in the next revision of the Concrete Data Manual [ 16 ] .

### PCCV Materials - Prestressing System
At Sizewell B, un-grouted tendons of the PSC Freyssinet K Series type were used to permit withdrawal and in-service inspection and re-stressing of tendons should this be required. Corrosion protection of the un-grouted tendons was provided by a factory applied corrosion protection system applied to the prestressing strand. Following installation of the tendons the ducts were filled with a corrosion inhibiting soft wax.

### Materials used on other Nuclear Safety Related Structures
The materials used in other nuclear safety related structures on the stations vary considerably and include structural steelwork, reinforced concrete, brickwork and blockwork. Material specifications have changed with time and on any particular station a range of materials to differing specifications will be present. Any assessment of these structures must therefore take account of the specification to which the structural materials were supplied at the time of construction or subsequent modification.

### In-service Inspections
It is the policy of BE to carry out condition monitoring and inspection of civil engineering structures on the nuclear power plants at frequencies and using methods that are appropriate to the importance of each structure to nuclear safety.

With regard to the condition monitoring of Civil Structures, a distinction may be drawn between this specialised form of surveillance and other types of structural survey. It is therefore useful to define these as follows:
- Condition Monitoring: In-service surveillance of structures on a continuous or quasi-continuous basis using imbedded or externally applied monitoring devices. This includes automated systems linked to data-logging equipment which may have pre-defined alarm levels.
- In-service inspection: In-service surveillance of structures by periodic surveys at specified intervals. This may include consideration of information obtained during condition monitoring surveys over the period between inspections.

The current practice in the UK Nuclear Industry is to limit the use of condition monitoring, as defined above, only to structures of high importance where relatively small changes of state may be of consequence to long term structural performance (i.e. PCPVs and PCCVs). This enables a high margin of safety to be maintained throughout the lifetime of such structures.

### Appointed Examiner

The procedure adopted by SN and NEL in compiling the statutory report for start-up following an outage on PCPVs and PCCVs is that the report is prepared by an Appointed Examiner(APEX) who is a nominated suitably qualified and experienced chartered civil or structural engineer who is also responsible for the implementation of the monitoring program and the assessment and reporting of the results which culminate in the start-up report.

The Appointed Examiner has a high level of civil engineering technical expertise, particularly with regard to the design, construction and ongoing behaviour of large concrete structures such as the PCPV's. Experience of structural monitoring augmented by specific on the job PCPV and PCCV training plus plant familiarisation is essential covering such topics as :-

- Overview of AGR Operation (or PWR operation)
- Design philosophy of PCPVs and PCCVs
- Familiarisation with the conditions of the Nuclear Site Licence
- Familiarisation with Station MITS/MS (or PCCV surveillance program)
- Station Safety Case
- Case History and Lifetime Records
- Quality Assurance procedures
- BS 4975 (PCPVs only)
- Design and Construction Rules for PWR Primary Containment (PCCV only)
- Safety Training
- Plant familiarisation

All work related to the structural monitoring of PCPVs is carried out under an approved Quality Assurance Program (QAP) which is subject to regular review. The QAP provides for the delegation of specific duties of the Appointed Examiner to personnel who meet appropriate training requirements. APEX is the collective term for the personnel tasked with the execution of in-service inspection activities relating to PCPVs as detailed in the QAP.

The QAP covers the managerial and procedural arrangements adopted to provide assurance that all those planned and systematic actions which contribute to the safe, effective operation of the nuclear power stations are controlled within statutory and regulatory requirements and design criteria. The arrangements, responsibilities, procedures and instructions in the QAP are mandatory on all APEX staff.
Each site is responsible for operating within the terms of its nuclear site licence and in relation to the PCPVs, issues a letter of appointment to the Appointed Examiner. At Sizewell B, this appointment covers the PCCV and also all safety related structures.

### PCPVs - Surveillance Program

All the inspections are completed in accordance with the requirements of the maintenance, inspection and test schedule (MITS) or Maintenance Schedule (MS) (depending on the station) which is an identified document under the compliance arrangements for the nuclear site licence conditions. All monitoring and assessment must be carried out by suitably qualified and experienced personnel and the results reviewed regularly and collated to provide a consolidated report. For the PCPVs and the PCCV this report must be available at the end of each statutory reactor outage to justify continued operation prior to NII consent for the reactor to return to power.

## PCPV Monitoring, Testing and Surveillance

The current revision of BS 4975 [ 11 ] contains a specific section (Section 9) on the testing and surveillance of these structures. Both the minimum range of inspections to be carried out and a supplementary set which may be used are covered. However, the full range of examinations is routinely carried out and reported by both Scottish Nuclear Ltd and Nuclear Electric plc.

| Minimum program: | Supplementary program: |
|---|---|
| • Tendon load checks | • Vibrating wire strain gauge readings |
| • Tendon anchorage examinations | • Concrete and liner temperature readings |
| • Concrete surface examinations | • Main reactor coolant leakage summaries |
| • Foundation settlement surveys | • PCPV deflection surveys |
| | • Operating history review |

+ tendon strand examination

## Prestressing System

The structural integrity of the PCPVs depends on the maintenance of an adequate level of prestress in the vessels and particular emphasis is placed on monitoring this. A minimum of 1% of the steel tendons are load checked at a frequency relevant for the reactor outages. The level of prestress reduces naturally with time due to relaxation so the results from sample load checks are used to monitor trends which can be extrapolated to end of life by plotting them against time in a log-linear format . By this means early warning would be given indicating that mean tendon loads are approaching the minimum values required by the design and remedial action can be taken to restore the prestress in the vessels.

The corresponding tendon load losses over the life of a station may be estimated by examination of material tests carried out over a period of 1000 hours. Experience has shown that the load loss in 18mm Dyform strand after 30 years will be approximately twice the loss at 1000 hours at 20 °C.  The losses experienced increase with increasing service temperature and so allowance must be made for this. At the load levels typically encountered in PCPV tendons the increase in loss at higher temperatures varies linearly between 20 °C and 80 °C with the value for the latter being approximately four times that for the former.

The tendon anchorage components are inspected for signs of deterioration and a number of lengths of prestressing strand are withdrawn for metallurgical and mechanical testing and comparison with the original specification. The withdrawn strand is closely inspected for evidence of corrosion or other defects. Corrosion may result from wetting due to leakage of the pressure vessel cooling water system cast within the vessel concrete or from external sources (for example, from ground water seepage). Additional inspections have also been carried out on the corrosion protection system for the tendons and their anchorage components which confirm that adequate protection is provided throughout the life of the PCPVs [ 17 ].

## PCPV Surface Examination
The surface of each PCPV is closely inspected to monitor and assess the significance of any cracking and the general condition of the concrete including the presence of any water leakage from the vessel cooling system. The results of these surveys are then recorded and a comparison made with previous surveys.

The presence of water leakage is treated seriously as it could be an indication that the integrity of the pressure vessel cooling system (PVCS) has been compromised. If any signs of leakage are detected, the leakage rate is recorded and an investigation carried out to determine the source of the water and the extent of remedial action to be taken.

Fine cracking and surface crazing has been noted to at the surface of the PCPVs due to drying shrinkage and thermal effects on the surface layer of the concrete. This tends to be exhibited at discontinuities around embedments. Such cracking may not be marked onto record drawings unless the crack width exceeds a specified value for the vessel. However, should cracks show unstable behaviour, be in a critical position or show an unusual pattern then they would be assessed by the Appointed Examiner.

## PCPV Settlement and Tilt
Precise optical levelling is carried out to determine the degree of settlement experienced by the structure and identify any differential settlement which may interfere with the operation of nuclear related plant and services. The type of foundation for the PCPVs varies with the type of vessel and the local ground conditions at each site. The tilt of the PCPVs is estimated from settlement results and a comparison is made against tilt limits which are based on assessment of the effects on the core and its support structure and the ability to insert the control rods.

## PCPV Top Cap Deflection
The precise optical levelling method is also used on all stations to measure the deflection of the top cap region of the vessel structure under depressurised and normal operating conditions and this is compared with measurements taken at the time of the vessel proof pressure test (PPT) performed during commissioning. Further measurements over a range of operating pressures have been taken on the Scottish Nuclear stations and from these and the standard measurements it can be confirmed that the vessels behave in a predictable linear elastic manner consistent with the results obtained at the PPT over the full range of pressures from the de-pressurised state to full working pressure and that there is no change in the structural response with time. At Hunterston B, Scottish Nuclear are considering the installation of an automated multi-point deflection monitoring system coupled to a dedicated electronic logging system.

## PCPV Vibrating Wire Strain Gauges
Embedded instrumentation is also used to monitor the vessels in the form of vibrating wire strain gauges (VWSGs). It should be noted, however, that in the majority of PCPVs the VWSGs were installed for use only during the commissioning Proof Pressure Test and were not intended for long term monitoring although they have subsequently been used for this purpose. The results of the strain gauge measurements are reviewed periodically and fully analysed at five yearly intervals for comparison with theoretical predictions. They provide a useful indication of elastic behaviour by the concrete during pressure cycles and long term creep effects but the results must be considered as being advisory only. To date the results of the VWSG measurements have shown a good correlation with expected values [ 18 ] .

### PCPV Temperature

Thermocouples are used to check that concrete and steel liner temperatures are maintained within the limits specified in the operating rules for the vessels and that there is no upward drift of temperature with time or excessively hot areas within the structure due to, for example, failure of the liner insulation. The maximum bulk concrete temperature is maintained within limits which ensure that the strength of the concrete is unaffected and that creep strain is minimised. The liner/concrete temperatures are maintained by the Pressure Vessel Cooling System (PVCS) which is attached to the concrete side of the steel liner close to the barrel liner.

In all AGR PCPVs the temperature differential between the concrete in the standpipe region and that in the surrounding concrete is limited to prevent differential expansion/contraction leading to a reduction in the compressive prestress in the standpipe region.

### PCPV Main Reactor Coolant Leakage

Measurements of main reactor coolant (carbon dioxide, $CO_2$) bulk leakage are regularly made by station staff and the results are periodically reviewed to check that the pressure boundary is intact and that hot gas cannot affect the performance of the main structure. In the Heysham II / Torness PCPV design additional allowance was made for measurement of $CO_2$ leakage by the provision of sixteen unlined vertical ducts which pass through the concrete. These ducts are checked regularly as part of the vessel monitoring regime.

The potential for carbon dioxide leakage in the various PCPV designs and the significance of this for vessel integrity has been the subject of specific assessments which were principally based on the effect of any leakage of hot coolant on prestressing tendons.

### PCCV - Surveillance Program

The Sizewell B PCCV does not have a MITS/MS in the same form as those used for the PCPVs. However, the in-service inspections carried out on the PCCV are covered by a surveillance program defined in the technical specification for the vessel.

### PCCV - Monitoring, Testing & Surveillance

Inspections of the PCCV and other related structures are carried out under the jurisdiction of the Appointed Examiner in accordance with the relevant sections of the surveillance program - *Rules for the In-Service Inspection of Civil Engineering Works - SXB-IC- 096556/3*.

In a similar manner to that employed for the inspection of the PCPVs, the levels of prestress in the PCCV are regularly checked, the tendon anchorage components and external concrete surface inspected, and during outages an inspection of the internal liner of the primary containment is completed. Levelling is carried out to determine the degree of settlement experienced by the PCCV and the other safety related structures; because of its marine pedigree, the PWR is not susceptible to tilt affecting the ability to insert the control rods.

Again similarly to the PCPVs, the PCCV includes imbedded instrumentation, installed to monitor its performance during construction and the structural over pressure test, which will be used to monitor its long term structural behaviour. This instrumentation comprises vibrating wire strain gauges and their associated thermocouples.

With regard to structural integrity, the main function of the PCCV is in conjunction with the liner and other systems, to prevent uncontrolled release to the environment of fission products. This is achieved by ensuring that the barrel and dome remain in overall compression, confirmed by the tendon load checks, and by the individual penetration local leak rate tests and the integrated leak rate test applied to the whole PCCV and which thereby checks the performance of the liner and its penetration closures.

## Nuclear safety related structures
A list of Safety Related Structures and procedures for the inspection each of them are prepared from examination of the Station Safety Report. The subsequent inspections of Safety Related Structures are carried out in accordance with Site Licence conditions 28 and 29, and the relevant Site Licence Compliance Arrangements.

The inspections are visual in the first instance and list defects arising from:
- Wear
- Corrosion
- Damage
- Leaks

- Poor original construction
- Mal-operation
- Ageing

All areas where structural failure could cause damage to, or failure of, nuclear safety related equipment are addressed within the inspection report.

## Method of Inspection
The inspection of each building or area is carried out using a list detailing the elements to be checked and is directed to the potential defects identified in Table 9 although the inspector is expected to note and record any other defects identified. Advice with regard to the inspections is obtained from standard industry publications and technical papers [ 1,2,19-27 ].

## Checklists
For each safety related structure identified in the schedule of inspections, a specific inspection procedure is drawn up. Checklists are prepared for each building or area of building from detail drawings and preliminary inspections. These include the relevant drawings plus more detailed descriptions of the buildings and give guidance for the inspection team. It is important before embarking on the inspection that the engineer knows, for example, whether walls are designed to resist blast loading, gas pressure loading or earthquake effects. This enables him to make a clear judgement on how to record any defects that may affect the safety case.
Therefore the procedure provides a clear explanation of the safety case for that particular area of the site and sufficient information to allow a proper inspection of the structure to be carried out. Each checklist is signed on completion by the Inspectors.

## Frequency of Inspection
The interval between inspections is generally 5 years. In specified areas the frequency may be increased to between 2 and 5 years particularly when the initial survey indicates that more frequent inspections are required. Any recommendations or requirements for a change to the frequency of inspection should be included in the inspection report.

## Defect Verification
The inspections are carried out by suitably qualified and experienced Engineers. The minimum qualification acceptable for Inspecting Engineers is Graduate Engineer, and for the

Responsible Engineer (i.e. Team Leader), Chartered Engineer, in Civil or Structural Engineering. Verification of all defects would mean that a separate second inspection would have to be carried out. Consequently only defects likely to lead to a nuclear safety hazard are to be re-inspected and confirmed by a Verification Team.

### Implementation of Any Repairs
A Working Party formed in conjunction with the Station staff initiate and supervise any remedial actions from the inspections. A master database of all the defects is held by the Station Manager who is responsible for tracking the completion of any proposed actions and ensuring compliance with the Station Safety Report.

### QUALITY ASSURANCE
In order to comply with the licence conditions, the company quality assurance system and to ensure a common approach throughout, written procedures are required. General procedures were developed for the inspections at each Station. All structural inspections are carried out under specific quality assurance procedures in accordance with the ISO 9000 series of standards which detail the scope and extent of the work, the manner in which it is to be carried out, the periodicity of inspections, the required qualifications and experience of the engineering staff involved and the method of reporting and recording the results of the surveys. The procedures contain a schedule of the nuclear safety related structures as defined in the Station safety cases at each site including summaries of the safety functions of the structures.

### ASSESSMENT CRITERIA
In some instances fixed acceptance criteria are specified (mainly for PCPVs and the PCCV) but in many areas this is not appropriate and the survey results are considered on an individual basis. Where fixed criteria are stated, it is important that the survey does not concentrate on these alone and that a general survey is carried out with identified observations being judged against the fixed criteria. This prevents the inspecting engineer from missing potential defects which could occur should his attention be solely fixed on defect types for which acceptance criteria exist. Guidance on the collection, interpretation and analysis of the results for acceptance or rejection is based on information and good practice obtained from a variety of sources ([ 9-24 ]). In particular, the methods used for the inspection of nuclear safety related structures are based on the recommendations of [ 1,2,11-15,19-27 ]. In particular, the reports by the Institution of Structural Engineers: "Guide to Surveys and Inspections of Buildings and Similar Structures" and "Appraisal of Existing Structures" provided useful guidance. Future issues will also note the advice contained in the second edition of the Institution of Structural Engineer's report on the appraisal of existing structures [ 25 ].

### STRUCTURAL EVALUATION
Historical records and databases and comparison with the performance of similar structures are used to identify the effects of ageing and any identified trending. Where necessary, re-analysis of the structures is carried out taking account of any modifications that have been made to the structures since construction and any subsequent changes in loading conditions and the requirements of design codes. Inspection and monitoring activities on the Nuclear Power Plants operated by Nuclear Electric and Scottish Nuclear over the last 25 years have allowed a pattern of behaviour to be established and any variance from the norm is subjected to detailed investigation. Major re-evaluation of structures is carried out during Periodic

Safety Reviews to demonstrate that the civil engineering structures on the stations are performing in accordance with the design intent.

## PERIODIC SAFETY REVIEW
The results of all inspections, including the statutory PCPV and PCCV reports and safety related structures survey reports, are collated and reviewed every ten years in a full Periodic Safety Review (PSR) of the plant. This review considers the original design intent and substantiation, commissioning (including the proof pressure tests and subsequent vessel operation), changes to standards applied since construction, the effects of ageing and deterioration, and an assessment of the ability of the structures to continue to fulfil their intended purpose. With regard to the last of these, a full assessment is completed against a range of potential hazards including fire, steam and hot gas release, dropped loads, missile impact, aircraft impact, flooding, seismic, wind, industrial hazards and extreme temperatures. Based on the results of the PSR, any requirements for modification or retro-fitting of safety related structures are identified and work programs for completion of the work developed. The PSR therefore provides a full review of the existing safety case and addresses any issues that need to be met for continued Station operation.

## ONGOING RESEARCH AND ANALYSIS
Ongoing research and analysis are undertaken to ensure that the mechanisms of structural ageing are fully understood to enable nuclear safety related structures to be maintained to the highest of standards. A Nuclear Research Index, containing a list of issues that it is considered would benefit from research activity, is prepared, reviewed and updated on an annual basis by the Health and Safety Executive (HSE).

The Health and Safety Commission (HSC) Co-ordinated Programme consists of research to address the safety issues presented in the Nuclear Research Index produced by HSE and takes into account research undertaken by the Licensees for their own purposes, by other government departments and elsewhere. The programme is managed by HSE on behalf of the HSC.

The HSC Co-ordinated Programme is concerned with nuclear safety research activity related to UK thermal reactor sites and comprises two elements:
- The HSE Levy Programme - that part of the HSC Co-ordinated Programme which is identified and placed by HSE and paid for through a levy on the Nuclear Licensees
- The Industry Management Committee (IMC) Programme - that part of the HSC Co-ordinated Programme which is identified, placed and paid for directly by the Nuclear Licensees

Through the Industry's Technical Working Groups, which consider specialist areas of investigation under the IMC, a programme of research into plant life management including structural ageing,   material studies, high temperature effects, and external hazard loadings including fire, steam and hot gas release, dropped loads, missile impact, aircraft impact, flooding, seismic, wind, industrial hazards and extreme temperatures

Research has been undertaken into formulating methods of assessing structural integrity of safety related concrete structures using finite element methods, which has involved an appraisal of a number of the 'state-of-the-art' finite element codes currently available for commercial use.

Difficulties associated with solution non-convergence have been identified and methods suggested for overcoming such difficulties. A framework has been produced to enable the engineer to assess the integrity of prestressed concrete vessels and containments by the use of non-linear analysis techniques, and the application of the original design concepts.

In such a way it has been possible to formulate an analysis strategy to investigate postulated over -pressurisation faults, for example, at pressures approaching the ultimate load condition.

## CONCLUSIONS

A comprehensive system of structural monitoring and testing is in place in the Nuclear Power Plants within the British Energy Group to ensure that nuclear safety is maintained.

The normal method of in-service surveillance of structures on nuclear power plants is by periodic surveys at specified intervals. This may include consideration of information obtained during condition monitoring surveys over the period between inspections where this is available as supporting information.

Condition monitoring involving the in-service surveillance of structures on a continuous or quasi-continuous basis using imbedded or externally applied monitoring devices is used when it is deemed necessary or advantageous. This may include automated systems linked to data-logging equipment which may have pre-defined alarm levels. However, the current practice in the UK Nuclear Industry is to limit the use of condition monitoring only to structures of high importance where relatively small changes of state may be of consequence to structural performance.

The experience gained with in-service structural inspection of PCPVs has been used in the development of surveillance programs covering other nuclear safety related structures and the Sizewell B PWR PCCV. The programs ensure that these structures fulfil their intended structural purpose in order to maintain nuclear safety and will continue to perform as intended over the life of the stations.

Inspection and monitoring activities on all the PCPVs operated by Nuclear Electric and Scottish Nuclear over the last 25 years have allowed a pattern of behaviour to be established and have demonstrated that they are performing in accordance with the design intent.

The in-service structural inspection of nuclear safety related structures has developed with time and will continue to do so. Developments in instrumentation, data processing and interpretation will enable more structures to be monitored more closely [ 28 & 29 ]. However, monitoring alone cannot be regarded as a panacea and the limitations of any system must be borne in mind particularly if heavy reliance is placed upon it to ensure safety. It is therefore important that continued research and development and periodic reviews are carried out in order that methods and procedures may be improved in the light of additional knowledge and technological advances.

Although the procedures discussed in this paper have been specifically developed for the in-service inspection of civil engineering structures on nuclear power plants, the basic principals involved and methods used could be applied to structures encountered on sites used by other industries and processes.

## REFERENCES

1.  Smith, LM, "In-service Monitoring of Nuclear Safety Related Structures", The Structural Engineer, Volume 74, No.12, 18 June 1996, Pages 210-211, The Institution of Structural Engineers, UK.
2.  MacFarlane, JP, Smith, LM, Davies, DR, and McCluskey, DT, "In-service Monitoring of AGR and PWR Nuclear Safety Related Structures in the UK", Institution of Nuclear Engineers, International Conference on Nuclear Containment, September 23-25 1996, Cambridge, UK
3.  "The Nuclear Installations Act 1965", HMSO, UK, 1965 (*et seq*)
4.  Bradford PM, and McNair, IJ, "A Regulatory View of Nuclear Containment on UK Licensed Sites", Institution of Nuclear Engineers, International Conference on Nuclear Containment, September 23-25 1996, Cambridge, UK
5.  "The Pressure Systems and Transportable Gas Containers Regulations 1989", Statutory Instruments, 1989 No. 2169 Health and Safety, HMSO, UK, 1989
6.  CP 114, "Code of Practice for the Structural Use of Reinforced Concrete in Buildings", British Standards Institution, London, UK, 1957
7.  CP 115, "Code of Practice for the Structural Use of Prestressed Concrete in Buildings", British Standards Institution, London, UK, 1959
8.  CP 110, "The Structural Use of Concrete", British Standards Institution, London, UK, 1972
9.  BS 8110, "British Standard Structural Use of Concrete", British Standards Institution, London, UK, 1985
10. BS 4975, "Specification for Prestressed Concrete Pressure Vessels for Nuclear Reactors", British Standards Institution, London, UK, 1973
11. BS 4975, "British Standard Specification for Prestressed Concrete Pressure Vessels for Nuclear Engineering", British Standards Institution, London, UK, 1990
12. ASME Boiler and Pressure Vessel Code, Section III, Division 2, "Code for Concrete Reactor Vessels and Containments", American Society of Mechanical Engineers, New York, USA, July 1995
13. Davies, DR and Ness, D, "Structural pressure testing of the Sizewell B Prestressed Concrete Containment Vessel", Institution of Nuclear Engineers, International Conference on Nuclear Containment, September 23-25 1996, Cambridge, UK
14. ACI 349-85, " Code Requirements for Nuclear Safety Related Concrete Structures", American Concrete Institute, Detroit, USA, 1985
15. ACI 318-89, "Building Code Requirements for Reinforced Concrete", American Concrete Institute, Detroit, USA, 1989
16. Grainger, BN, Johnston MW and Pritchard, JA, "Concrete Data Manual R77", Issue 1, March 1994, Nuclear Electric plc, Gloucester, UK
17. Smith, LM and Taylor, MF, "The Long Term In-service Performance of Corrosion Protection to Prestressing Tendons in AGR Prestressed Concrete Pressure Vessels", Joint WANO/OECD Workshop on Prestress Losses in NPP Containments, 25-26 August 1997, Civaux, France
18. Smith, LM and Irving, J, "The In-service Strain Response of Prestressed Concrete Pressure Vessels for Advanced Gas-cooled Reactors", International Association for Structural Mechanics in Reactor Technology, 14th International Conference on

Structural Mechanics in Reactor Technology, Paper 236, Session H01 : In Situ Tests and Monitoring, 17-22 August 1997, Lyon, France.

19.    "An International Survey of In-service Inspection Experience with Prestressed Concrete Pressure Vessels and Containments for Nuclear Reactors", Federation Internationale de la Precontrainte, Slough, UK, April 1982

20.    ASME Boiler and Pressure Vessel Code, Section XI, "Rules for In-service Inspection of Nuclear Power Plant Components", American Society of Mechanical Engineers, New York, USA, July 1995

21.    "FIP Guide to Good Practice, Inspection and Maintenance of Reinforced and Prestressed Concrete Structures", Federation Internationale de la Precontrainte, Slough, UK, 1986

22.    "Guide to Surveys and Inspections of Buildings and Similar Structures", Institution of Structural Engineers, London, UK, 1992

23.    "Appraisal of Existing Structures (First Edition)", Institution of Structural Engineers, London, UK, October 1980

24.    BS 8210, " British Standard Guide to Building Maintenance Management", British Standards Institution, London, UK, 1986

25.    "Appraisal of Existing Structures (Second Edition)", Institution of Structural Engineers, London, UK, October 1996

26.    Moore, JFA, "Monitoring Building Structures", Van Nostrand Reinhold, New York, USA, 1992

27.    ACI 349.3R-96, "Evaluation of Existing Nuclear Safety Related Concrete Structures", American Concrete Institute, Detroit, USA, 1986

28.    Moss, RM and Matthews, SL, "In-service Structural Monitoring - a State of the Art Review", The Structural Engineer, Volume 73, No.2, 17 January 1995, Pages 23-31, The Institution of Structural Engineers, UK.

29.    Moss, RM and Matthews, SL, " Discussion - In-service Structural Monitoring - a State of the Art Review", The Structural Engineer, Volume 73, No.13, 4 July 1995, Pages 14-217, The Institution of Structural Engineers, UK.

30.    Davies, DR, and Kitchener, JN, "Massive use of Pulverised Fuel Ash in Concrete for the Construction of a UK Power Station", Waste Management, Volume 16, Number 1-3, 1996, Pages 169 - 180

*Theme 2:*

# Strategies for Maintenance and Serviceability

# Strategies for Maintenance and Long-Term Serviceability of Concrete Structures

JOHN MENZIES PhD FEng FIStructE
John B Menzies, Watford, United Kingdom

## SYNOPSIS

The management of concrete structures for long-term serviceability may be seen as part of the struggle against inevitable disorder. The engineering of new concrete structures is essentially concerned with creating order in a world where there is a universal tendency towards disorganisation. That work has to be done not only to create such organisation but also to maintain it, has been common experience for many centuries.

Concrete structures are not exempt from the universal tendency towards disorganisation. Although they may have substantial durability compared to a human lifespan, appropriate maintenance and repair (and sometimes refurbishment, alteration and strengthening) are generally essential to enable long-term serviceability and an optimum return from the original input of resources. The paper outlines the principles which may be used to meet this objective with particular reference to building and bridge structures.

The existing stock of concrete structures in the UK is large and ageing. A wide range of factors influence the choice of strategies for achieving their long-term serviceability. Major influences are the ownership of the structure, whether the owner has a large or small stock of similar concrete structures, their function, whether they are fulfilling their function, the consequences of the loss of function, forecast future needs for them and the severity of the service environment. Some approaches to strategies are discussed in the context of current technology and referring to current practice mainly using, as examples, building and bridge structures.

## OBJECTIVE

The objective of this paper is to identify the basic elements and principles for developing strategies for the maintenance and long-term serviceability of a single concrete structure and of stocks of similar structures.

## INTRODUCTION

The management of concrete structures for long-term serviceability may be seen as part of the struggle against inevitable disorder. The engineering of new concrete structures is essentially concerned with creating order in a world where there is a universal tendency towards disorganisation. It has been recognised experience for many centuries that work has to be done not only to create such organisation but also to maintain it. The well-known words '.... Upon earth... moth and rust doth corrupt and ... thieves break through and steal...' graphically describes it. Modern science has given us the same message using the concept of entropy - the scientist's measure of disorder - in the second law of thermodynamics. A seventeenth century

*Management of concrete structures for long-term serviceability*. Thomas Telford, London, 1997

Italian treatise exhorted 'The architect, soon after any building is completed, must not forget it, but must get around it with great care to preserve it....'.

Concrete structures are not exempt from the universal tendency towards disorganisation. Although they may have substantial durability compared to a human lifespan, appropriate maintenance and repair (and sometimes refurbishment, alteration and strengthening) are generally essential to enable long-term serviceability and safety and an optimum return from the input of resources. The management objective may be expressed as the definition and implementation of the optimum strategy that ensures adequate reliability of the structure at the lowest possible life-cycle cost. For a particular structure it is best expressed in terms of the needs of the owner, ie. a strategy for maintenance to ensure future serviceability in the most cost effective way meeting the owner's requirements. Appropriate strategies to meet this objective depend on a wide range of factors. A major influence on the choice of strategy is whether the owner or owners have a single structure or a stock of similar concrete structures.

Ideally the strategy for maintenance and long-term serviceability of a structure is decided during its initial procurement. This situation did not often obtain for structures in the current large stock of existing concrete structures in the United Kingdom. Generally for existing structures, the need is to determine a strategy where none has previously been defined, or where an earlier strategy now needs review in the light of changed circumstances. This paper focuses therefore on these more usual situations.

The existing stock of concrete structures in the UK is large and ageing. It is a very valuable national asset. There is an increasing need for engineers to find ways of extending the lifespans of the structures in this stock whilst maintaining safety and observing tight cost constraints. The definition and use of cost effective strategies for maintenance and long-term serviceability would be a major contribution to meeting the need.

## THREATS TO CONCRETE STRUCTURES
Samples of sound Roman and Chinese 'concrete' can be found which are over 2000 years old. These materials have survived because they have been in a benign and stable environment usually arising from the protective influence of surrounding masonry. The structures in which they are found are either largely dilapidated and not fulfilling their original function or they have been substantially repaired and rebuilt over their lifetimes. Other similar structures have not survived because they have suffered deterioration and instability, accidental or deliberate damage or replacement by new structures to meet new requirements.

This general experience serves to illustrate a number of factors which are important in determining strategies for achieving long-term serviceability and safety of modern concrete structures:

- Individual concrete structures deteriorate over time in a non-uniform way, ie. those parts most susceptable to deterioration and/or exposed to the most aggressive conditions deteriorating much more rapidly than parts which are more durable or less threatened by their surroundings.
- Long-term serviceability and safety may be threatened by increased loading over time, by events causing instability (eg. foundation movement or overloading), and by accidental damage (eg. vehicle impact) or deliberate damage (eg vandalism)

- Structures do not necessarily need to have an indefinitely long life (although some types of concrete construction can have a very long life given appropriate repair and maintenance) since they may only be required for a limited period or, even though made exceptionally durable, may not be able to meet future functional requirements.

Some common types of deterioration in reinforced concrete are:

- Corrosion of reinforcement causing cracking and spalling of the concrete cover - may arise as a result of high contents of free chloride ions in the concrete or of loss of alkalinity of the concrete due to its carbonation.
- Corrosion of prestressing tendons causing, if pretensioned, cracking of the concrete cover and, if post-tensioned by steel tendons in ducts, loss of tension without warning signs - may arise from presence of chlorides or carbonation and exposure of tendons to air and moisture.
- Freeze - thaw damage caused by freezing whilst wet especially if concrete contains inadequate entrained air.
- Alkali - silica reaction causing characteristic crack patterns in the concrete.
- Sulphate attack causing disruption of the concrete and arising from, for example, rock salt used to de-ice roads.
- Accidental impact may remove concrete cover to reinforcement making it vulnerable to corrosion.

Corrosion of reinforcement or tendons is the most common form of deterioration of concrete structures. This form is therefore used in this paper to illustrate strategy development.

## DEVELOPING A STRATEGY
The owner's requirements for the future use of a structure form the context within which a strategy for maintenance is developed. The history of the structure and its current condition must be determined first to provide a basis for assessment and prediction of its future performance in service. The consideration of options to enable the structure to meet future serviceability requirements then follows. The process should lead to the choice of the most cost effective option and result in the overall strategy.

The principles to be followed are generally the same irrespective of the type of structure, eg. bridge or building. The elements of the process of strategy development for a particular structure are illustrated in Figure 1 and each is discussed below.

In developing a strategy it may be helpful to divide threats to serviceability into categories:

- Deterioration of the structural materials arising from the surrounding environment existing when the structure is built.
- Deterioration processes which are accelerated or retarded through changes in the environment over time. It is important to recognise that environmental changes over time may activate new forms of deterioration of materials or more rapid deterioration through a process hitherto virtually dormant.
- Effects due to changes in loads which the structure is required to carry, eg increased traffic loads on bridges or storage of heavier goods in buildings.

- Structural effects due to changes in the surroundings, eg. for a bridge over a river, civil engineering work upstream or downstream modifying the river flow and causing scour of the pier foundations.
- Potentials for accidental or deliberate damage.

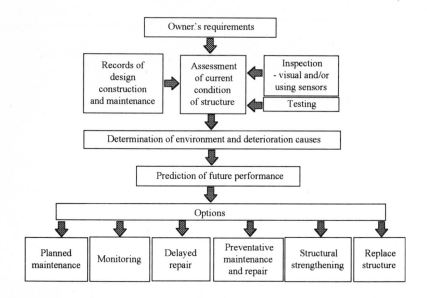

Figure 1. Development of a maintenance sttrategy for a single concrete structure

## OWNERS REQUIREMENTS

In many cases the owner will desire long-term serviceability, the emphasis being on achievement at minimum cost. There may also be constraints on maintenance and repair works arising from needs to avoid interference with the on-going use of the structure. A further constraint may be the availability of finance for the works to the optimum time scales from a technical point of view.

Additional considerations may arise where a strategy is required for the maintenance of a stock of similar structures, eg. Airey houses, or diverse structures with a common function, eg. highway bridges over major and minor roads. Several or even a large number of owners may be involved and the structures may collectively be a vital part of regional or national infrastructure. In these circumstances the use of a common strategy is desirable especially if a defect with safety implications has been found in one of the structures. Organisational barriers arising from owner's interests, governmental, commercial or local practices may impede use of a common strategy. Financial and other constraints may prevent prioritisation and optimal implementation of maintenance and repair works.

# HISTORY AND CURRENT CONDITION

## Determining current condition

In view of the unknowns in the history of use of any structure, the non-uniform nature of the deterioration of concrete structure, the variety of deterioration processes which may be present, and the potential variations in the quality of the original construction, it is essential first to determine current condition. A site survey of the structure and examination of documentary information are the starting points for this purpose.

For building structures the Institution of Structural Engineers has provided concise guidance on structural appraisal[1]. The guidance describes the steps necessary (including survey, inspection and testing) to determine the details of the construction and its condition.

## Determination of service environment and causes of deterioration

It is essential to determine the service environment to which the structure has been, or is likely to be, subjected and the causes of any deterioration or defects which may be found. Without this information, a sound strategy for maintenance cannot be developed. The Institution's guidance[1] therefore provides extensive information on types of defect and on investigation and test techniques which may be used to check the visual evidence.

As part of the task of determining current condition, it is also necessary to assess loadings and to appraise the robustness, strength and serviceability of the structure in relation to them. This cyclical process, described for building structures in the Institution of Structural Engineers report and illustrated by flowcharts [1], needs to be pursued until a clear view of load carrying capacity is obtained. More refined input data, eg. on material strengths or dimensions, and structural analyses are used in each successive cycle in order to take advantage, where needed, of reserves of capacity ignored in the first cycle which consists of simple calculations using conservative values for input data. The guidance on calculations uses limit state concepts and the use of partial factors. The care needed when making use of out-of-date Codes of Practice for design which were current at the time of construction is discussed. Test techniques which can be used to improve the information on the nature and properties of the structural materials and on the response of the structure to load are described.

For bridges (and also other types of structure), the principles which are used for assessment of load carrying capacity are similar to those adopted for building structures. However differences in emphasis arise because of the essentially dynamic nature of traffic loading, the exposure of the structure and its generally more severe service environment. Standards for the assessment of highway bridges are included within the Design Manual for Roads and Bridges (DMRB)[2]. These standards refer to DMRB standards for design and for site survey and testing. They are based on the national bridge design code BS5400, where appropriate, but use modified rules to take account of the differences in assessment compared to design.

For railway bridges, there are Railway Group Standards for examination of structures [3] and assessment of structural capacity [4]. Their purpose is primarily to enable the risk of total or partial failure to be minimised and to maintain route carrying capacities. This emphasis is a recognition of the priority given to safety and that acceptable risk of bridge failure creating a hazard to railway operations is very low. These standards refer to the stock of structures as a whole. They provide the basis for internal standards established by the owners of railway bridges. As a whole the standards concentrate on ensuring that each structure receives regular examination, and adequate records are kept of the details of the structure, the frequency and results of examinations, and the findings of assessments. The guidance on capacity assessment states that assessments are only one part of the process to ensure structural integrity, other major parts being examination, maintenance, repair or renewal. The development of a long-term strategy for this process is not discussed although relevant guidance is in the internal standards. Development of overall strategy is implicitly within the overall responsibility of the appropriate manager.

### Prediction of future performance
The history of the structure, testing and structural appraisal provide the basis for assessment of its current condition including the causes of defects and deterioration. The next step is to develop a prediction of future performance in the light of options for future maintenance and the owner's requirements. For concrete structures it is necessary to make predictions of the future severity and consequences of significant deterioration which has been found in the determination of current condition. Many deterioration mechanisms, eg. corrosion or chloride ingress, may vary widely in their rates of progression. Predictions of future use of the structure and its loading should also be taken into account in relation to its robustness, strength and serviceability.

## OPTIONS FOR INDIVIDUAL STRUCTURES
Determination of an optimum strategy requires consideration of available options for maintenance in the light of the assessment of current condition, initial maintenance costs and future costs. For any structure the available options may be divided into several types:

> Planned maintenance
> Monitoring
> Delayed repair
> Preventative maintenance and repair
> Structural strengthening
> Replace structure

### Planned maintenance
Maintenance manuals may exist for some modern buildings which specify inspections of items such as plant and electrical equipment and exposed steelwork. Inspections are generally specified for services or fabric where maintenance is expected and should cover all components which may have a limited life, eg sealants, flat roofs. Inspection intervals should be based on expected life and needs for repair. Inspection of the condition of the reinforced concrete structure of a building is desirable, even if it is hidden behind fabric.

The concept of planned maintenance of buildings is that maintenance and repair is based on visual inspection and scheduled such that the building is kept in good condition. For concrete building structures its application in practice appears generally not to be comprehensive. It is nevertheless a viable option for concrete structures and can be effective over the long term particularly if inspections of key elements of structure are specified and monitoring systems are installed within the concrete structure to give early warning of significant progressive deterioration.

### Monitoring
The assessment of current condition may have identified the onset of deterioration and identified the causes. Future rates of chloride ion ingress or carbonation can be estimated, for

example, using predictive calculations as a basis for deciding future inspection locations and timescales. At the same time it may be decided to apply protective treatments to reduce deterioration rates. Monitoring provides a means of identifying future deterioration.

Traditionally monitoring is by visual inspection but today many aspects of the condition of reinforced concrete can be monitored using probes linked to remote logging systems. Such systems will record measurements and also trigger alarms when preset criteria are exceeded, eg movement. Monitoring is particularly valuable where loadings are expected to increase in the future, or where available repair techniques are likely only to reduce deterioration rates and continuing deterioration may be expected.

### Delayed repair

Traditionally maintenance strategy has been to make repairs immediately following assessment of condition. However reliability methods are now emerging which enable repair to be delayed until the optimum times. They are based on analyses of rates of deterioration and the costs of different strategies for maintenance and repair (Figure 2).

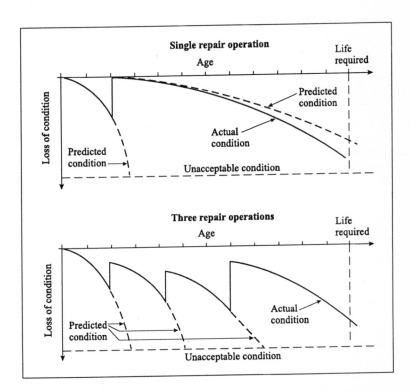

Figure   2.   Alternative   repair   strategies   for   a   reinforced   concrete   structure

The cost of concrete repair work itself is a small proportion of the total cost of a repair contract (reported typically to be about 20-30 per cent for patch repairs of a concrete building). The lowest cost, on a life cycle cost basis, may not be obtained by carrying out repairs immediately but by doing so after perhaps one, two or five years. To determine the optimum time for repair, the deterioration processes for the structure are examined and future changes in condition are modelled. The analyses provide estimates of time to corrosion and time to spalling for each element of the structure.

The input data for the analyses are provided by the inspection and testing undertaken prior to the assessment of current condition The measurements are perforce local in character, ie at points on the structure, and therefore only provide an indication of the condition of the structure as a whole. Reliability concepts can be applied to this data to produce a predictive model for the elements of the structure from which the future reliability of the structure can be predicted with a higher degree of confidence.[6]

Serviceability limits may need also to be taken into account. For external facades of buildings, areas of spalling may require immediate repair because of the risk to people below from falling pieces of concrete or because of a public perception that the building is unsafe. In some cases structural inadequacy may demand immediate repair, eg structural analysis may reveal that loss of area of steel reinforcement in a major structural element has already reached the point where its load-carrying capacity is inadequate.

Substantial efforts are now being made to develop optimal reliability-based inspection and maintenance strategies for concrete structures, particularly in bridge engineering [5,6,7]. The resulting developments are likely to be an increasing influence on future strategies for concrete structures.

### Preventative maintenance and repair
Preventative action is designed to halt or, more realistically, to slow down the deterioration processes which are found to be at work. For a particular structure many possible options for preventative repair may exist depending on :

- what future maintenance works can be accepted
- the future life required of the structure
- foreseen changes of use of the structure requiring maintenance or possible strengthening works
- possibilities for access to the structure
- the deterioration processes to be inhibited - for chloride contaminated concrete, cathodic protection or chloride extraction may be used, for example, in addition to repairing the damaged concrete and reinforcement.

When specifying preventative maintenance and repair, it is particularly important to bear the owners requirements in mind, eg long-term maintenance-free repair is not appropriate where redevelopment of the building is foreseen in the near future. Neither should short-term repair be used if a long future life is required.

A wide variety of materials and systems is available for concrete repair. Standards describing options and concrete repair systems are being developed[8].

## Structural strengthening

Changes in loading requirements or regulations may lead to a need to strengthen a structure alongside actions to maintain its long-term serviceability, eg strengthening of highway bridges to accommodate increased traffic loading from 1999 under new EU Directives for transport. Options available for increasing the load-carrying capacity of existing structures include post-tensioning and externally-bonded reinforcement (steel plate or carbon fibre). Replacement of parts of the existing structure, particularly if the parts are deteriorated due to corrosion, may be an attractive option which at the same time will improve future durability, eg breaking out existing bars and replacing them, adding others and reinstating the concrete cover with new materials.

## Replacement structure

The prediction for the residual life of the structure may suggest that replacement may be cheaper than reusing the existing structure with continuing high maintenance costs. It is important to review critically the results of the assessment of current condition and the prediction to make sure that this conclusion is correct.

There may also be incentives towards replacement because the use of the existing structure is constrained, eg limited storey heights in buildings or clearance in bridges. The owner's requirements for the future life and use of the structure are especially crucial in deciding on this option.

## OPTIONS FOR STOCKS OF SIMILAR STRUCTURES

Similar structures may be defined as those which have at least one common feature. For example, a common material of construction such as reinforced concrete, common elements such as prestressed concrete beams, or a common function such as railway bridges may identify a group of similar structures. The development of a strategy for an individual structure in a group may follow the options already described but there may be in addition a need to consider the group as a whole. Some circumstances in which consideration of the group is required are:

- where the whole or part of the group is in the hands of a single owner, eg railway underbridges.
- a shortcoming is identified in an individual structure which has implications for the safety of other structures in the group
- the current condition and assessment of an individual structure has implications for the prediction of future performance of the group as a whole.

## Similar structures with a single owner

A single owner of similar structures will generally want to consider the maintenance burdens arising from the group as a whole. Since the structures have a single owner, organisational barriers to the development of a strategy for maintenance of the group as a whole are minimal. The owner is able to set standards, recognising relevant legislation and current industry practice as appropriate, and to define an optimum maintenance programme from his point of view. The development of the strategy will need to take into account the current condition of the whole group by analysis of :

- the age profile of the structures and the immediate needs for maintenance of individual structures in the group, including any identified shortcomings with safety implications. This consideration may be a major factor determining the priorities of the maintenance programme, eg high priority would be required for maintenance and repair of concrete structures where a hazard from falls of spalling concrete has been found.

- the remaining life of the structures before further deterioration creates an unacceptable risk to public safety
- the structural adequacy of the structures in relation to the owner's future needs for load-carrying capacity and service life.
- the use of the structures and constraints on removal from use and on access for maintenance
- options for maintenance and repair in relation to costs and profile of total spend over time.

### *Similar structure with different owners*

Where similar structures are in the hands of different owners, shortcomings identified in a single structure can also lead to the need for assessment and maintenance amongst the group of structures as a whole. The need arises especially where the shortcoming poses a risk or a suspected risk, to public safety which may also be present in other structures in the group.

Stocks of similar building structures in which such concerns for safety have arisen over recent decades include :

- Intergrid buildings of prestressed concrete[9]
- High alumina cement concrete in buildings[10]
- Airey houses[11] and other types of prefabricated concrete house construction[12]
- Large concrete panel system-built flats[13]

A characteristic of these stocks of buildings was that several thousand structures were usually involved and that most were owned originally by the public sector. The concerns identified were essentially related to deterioration of materials. Once the shortcoming had been identified in an individual structure, the need was to develop a strategy for determining whether it was present in the group as a whole, what safety or other issues arose, and what action was then necessary given a prediction of the future performance for the group as a whole.

An important aim was to avoid causing unnecessary public alarm concerning the safety of the structures whilst the group was assessed, a prediction developed and available options considered. Whilst organisational barriers tend to prevent coordinated action in these circumstances, it is clearly desirable for the owners involved to work together to maintain public confidence and to resolve the concerns. An overall strategy is needed for such situations. An effective strategy may need to include the preparation of authoritative technical guidance which all owners then follow as a common standard for condition assessment, remedial actions, and future maintenance. When safety is an issue the preparation of such guidance may need to involve relevant official and/or professional bodies, eg Department of the Environment or Institution of Structural Engineers, depending on political, financial and management considerations. In any particular case, the strategy used will depend principally upon the owner's requirements, the role of the stock as a national asset and part of the infrastructure, and the safety and operational implications of any structural shortcomings found.

## CONCLUSIONS

The long-term serviceability of concrete structures is inevitably threatened by various types of deterioration which generally occur in a non-uniform way. Serviceability may also be threatened by increases of loading, by events causing instability, by damage or by requirements for change of function.

The existing stock of concrete structures is ageing and resources to maintain it are becoming scarcer. The efficient use of these resources is becoming increasingly important.

A strategy for maintenance and future serviceability of an individual concrete structure should be developed in the context of the owner's requirements for its future use. The strategy should be based on consideration of its current condition and the available options, ie planned maintenance, monitoring, delayed repair, preventative maintenance, structural strengthening, or replace structure, to produce the most cost effective solution. Future strategies are increasingly likely to be reliability-based in pursuit of the most efficient use of resources.

For groups of similar structures additional considerations may arise depending on the ownership of the group (single or many owners) and on whether shortcomings found in individual structures have implications for structural safety and/or the future life of the group as a whole. To be effective in maintaining public confidence, especially where safety may be a concern, strategies for these situations generally need to include collaboration between owners working to common standards for condition assessment, remedial actions and future maintenance. The standards may need to include authoritative official and/or professional guidance.

## ACKNOWLEDGEMENTS

The author gratefully acknowledges helpful discussions with many engineers on topics outlined in this paper and especially the discussions within the Institution of Structural Engineers' Task Group on Appraisal of Existing Structures.

## REFERENCES

1.  Appraisal of existing structures, Institution of Structural Engineers, London, London, 1996
2.  Design Manual for Roads and Bridges, Volume 3, Section 4 :
    - BD21/93: The assessment of highway bridges and structures (replaced by BD21/97 in February 1997)
    - BD21/97 : The assessment of highway bridges and structures
    - BD34/90 : Technical requirements for the assessment and strengthening programme for highway structures - Stage 1 - Older short span bridges and retaining structures
    - BD44/95 : The assessment of concrete highway bridges and structures
    - BD46/92 : Technical requirements for the assessment and strengthening programme for highway structures - Stage 2 - Modern short span bridges
    - BD50/92 : Technical requirements for the assessment and strengthening programme for highway structures - Stage 3 - Long span bridges
    - BD56/90 : The assessment of steel highway bridges and structures
    - BD61/96 : The assessment of composite highway bridges and structures
    - BA16/97 : The assessment of highway bridges and structures

- BA34/90 : Technical requirements for the assessment and strengthening programme for highway structures: Stage 1 - Older short span bridges and retaining structures
- BA38/93 : Assessment of the fatigue life of corroded or damaged reinforcing bars
- BA44/96 : The use of BD 44/90 for the assessment of concrete highway bridges and structures
- BA 54/94 : Load testing for bridge assessment
- BA 55/94 :  The assessment of bridge substructures and foundations, retaining walls and buried structures
- BA 56/96 : The use of BD56 for the assessment of steel highway bridges and structures
- BA 61/96 : The use of BD 61 for the assessment of composite highway bridges and structures

3.  Railway Group Standard GC/RT 5121: Examination of structures, June 1995
4.  Railway Group Standard GC/RT 5141: Assessment of structural capacity: June 1995.
5.  Thoft-Christensen, P and Hansen, H I : Optimal strategy for maintenance of concrete bridges using expert systems. Proceedings ICOSSAR 93, Innsbruck, Austria, August 1993.
6.  The safety of bridges : flexibility, risks and options in design, assessment and management. International Symposium, Institution of Civil Engineers, London, 1996.
7.  Structural reliability in bridge engineering : design, inspection, rehabilitation and management. Proceedings, Workshop, Boulder, 1996, McGraw-Hill.
8.  prEN1504 : Products and systems for the protection and repair of concrete structures
9.  The structural condition of Intergrid buildings of prestressed concrete. Building Research Establishment. Report, HMSO, 1978.
10.  Bate, S C C : High alumina cement concrete in existing building structures. Building Research Establishment Report, HMSO, 1984.
11.  Airey Houses : technical information and guidance. Building Research Establishment, 1982.
12.  The structural condition of prefabricated reinforced concrete houses designed before 1960. Compendium of Reports, Ref. AP25. Building Research Establishment, 1987.
13.  The structure of Ronan Point and other Taylor Woodrow-Anglian buildings. Building Research Establishment, 1985.

# IAEA Co-ordinated Research Programme on Ageing Management of Concrete Containment Buildings

DR RICHARD JUDGE PhD MIMechE
AEA Technology, 329, Harwell, Didcot , Oxon OX11 0RA

## SYNOPSIS

A generic framework for ageing management of concrete containments in nuclear power plants has been developed as part of an IAEA Co-ordinated Research Programme (CRP). This forms the main theme of this paper. It is put into context by opening the paper with background to the CRP's activities, world-wide operating experience and current ageing management practice. The CRP's ageing management framework reflects existing best practice, and thus tends to cover activities that are already carried out in some IAEA Member States (including the UK). The paper concludes by looking ahead, with a brief consideration of potential near and medium term developments in ageing management of concrete containments.

## INTRODUCTION

### IAEA Co-ordinated Research Programme

Recognising the importance of effective ageing management programmes for nuclear power plants, the IAEA initiated work in the mid 1980's to increase awareness and understanding of ageing and its potential impact on plant safety. This work has progressively addressed significant safety related components in a nuclear plant.

Studies on concrete containments[1] began in late 1992, with the IAEA initiating a 'Co-ordinated Research Programme' (CRP). The CRP provides a mechanism for collaboration between a number of international researchers, with the aim of drawing on their collective experience to progress technical development and/or establish best practice in a specific area. In this case, the two over-arching objectives were the identification of dominant ageing mechanisms and the development of an effective strategy for managing ageing effects caused by the identified mechanisms. Sub-objectives, which addressed specific tasks within this overall remit, were also defined. The CRP has now completed its work and reported its findings [1,2].

When the IAEA initiated these studies (in 1992), there was considerable international variation in the extent to which ageing of containment buildings and other civil structures was being proactively managed. For example:

- In the UK, ageing management programmes were established for prestressed concrete pressure vessels and were being developed for other safety related structures;

---

[1] In the IAEA studies, we adopted the term 'concrete containment building' (CCB) to represent the varying designs of leaktight concrete structures used as part of containment systems in nuclear power plants world-wide. In this paper, reference to 'containments' implicitly covers all containment types included in the IAEA work.

*Management of concrete structures for long-term serviceability*. Thomas Telford, London, 1997

- In the US an extensive research programme was underway [3], and various groups (e.g. ACI, ASME) were in the process of developing relevant guidelines. Similarly, a wide programme addressing ageing management of all safety related concrete structures in a nuclear plant was being developed by Canadian utilities [ 4].
- In many other IAEA member states, although routine inspection of containments was being carried out, ageing issues had yet to be formally addressed.

The CRP members saw a particular need to provide information of value to utilities/ operators in implementing ageing management programmes for their containments, drawing on the knowledge of international practice and experience available to the CRP. This led to the definition of a generic framework for systematic ageing management of concrete containments.

The paper begins by providing a brief review of world-wide operating experience and current ageing management practice. It continues by describing the framework for an 'Ageing Management Strategy' developed by the CRP. The paper concludes by considering near and medium term developments in ageing management practice. It should also be noted that this paper presents a subset of the CRP's work; the CRP report [1] also includes reviews of degradation mechanisms, inspection and repair techniques, of on-going research and of ageing management practice for both nuclear and non-nuclear structures.

## OPERATING EXPERIENCE & AGEING MANAGEMENT PRACTICE

As part of its work, the CRP sent a questionnaire to all nuclear plant operators in IAEA member states, requesting information on the through life performance of the containment (in particular whether there had been any experience of age related degradation) and ageing management practice. Responses were received from 41 owners/operators representing 154 nuclear units [2]. In order to supplement this information, the CRP members also compiled documented examples of containment degradation (together with remedial measures) and summarised ageing management practice and on-going research in their own countries.

The following sections present key findings. More detailed information is given in Ref. [1].

### Degradation Experience

The performance of concrete containments in nuclear power plants world-wide has generally been good. In some cases, however, routine inspection has led to the detection of flaws which, if undetected, could have progressively impaired safety functions. Details are included in Reference [1], with documented examples including:
- low 28-day compressive strengths
- voids under the prestressing tendon bearing plates resulting from improper concrete placement
- cracking of prestressing tendon anchorheads due to stress corrosion or embrittlement
- containment dome delaminations due to low quality aggregate materials and absence of radial steel reinforcement or unbalanced prestressing forces.

Other construction-related problems with containments have included excessive voidage or honeycombing in the concrete, cold joints, cadweld (steel reinforcement connector) deficiencies, materials out of specification, higher than code-allowable concrete temperatures, exposure to freezing temperatures during concrete curing, misplaced steel reinforcement, prestressing system buttonhead deficiencies, and water-contaminated corrosion inhibitors.

Incidences of age-related degradation have also been reported. Examples include excessive containment building leakage, corrosion of prestressing tendon wires, leaching of tendon gallery concrete, prestress loss, and leakage of corrosion inhibitors from tendon sheaths. Other related problems include cracking and spalling of containment dome concrete due to freeze-thaw damage, low strengths of tendon wires, contamination of corrosion inhibitors by chlorides, and corrosion of concrete containment liners.

Cracking of the concrete and corrosion of the reinforcement were the most frequently reported symptoms of degradation reported in the IAEA survey results. About 30% of these instances were attributed to design or construction deficiencies. In the majority of cases of cracking reported in the survey, engineering assessments showed that no repair action was necessary.

In all the cases of degradation cited above, the relevant plant operator has either demonstrated that no action was required or has successfully implemented remedial action to restore the functionality of the containment to acceptable levels (i.e. in line with national regulatory requirements). Although no information was given on the cost of remedial action, this would have been significant if the work lengthened regular refuelling outages (a day of lost generation runs into hundreds of thousands of pounds).

### Containment Testing and Inspection
The containment provides the final physical barrier against the release of radioactive material to the outside environment. It has major safety significance, and is subject to routine inspections/tests to provide confidence in its continued integrity.

The inspection/test methods used by utilities are broadly comparable. Visual inspections and checks on tendon loads and corrosion (post-tensioned structures) provide assurance of integrity of the main components of the containment, with integrated leakage-rate tests providing demonstration of the containment's overall leaktightness. These methods are typically prescribed by national codes (standards) or regulations; the CRP's survey indicated that only a few owners used methods beyond those normally associated with code requirements.

For ease of plant access and reduced radiation and temperature levels, inspections are generally performed during planned outages. Inspection intervals or frequencies are determined based on requirements contained in codes and standards [e.g. Ref. 5]. These typically require early life inspections to provide confidence in quality of design and construction, followed by increasing intervals for the periodic through-life inspections which provide demonstration of continued integrity.

Although relatively few containments are heavily instrumented, it was noted by the CRP that results from automated monitoring have proved to be very effective in demonstrating continued compliance with design. Instrumentation has also provided valuable data for trending containment behaviour. Longer intervals (5 and 10 years) between inspections were usually associated with owners using instrumentation, supplemental inspection techniques, or other methods to augment the visual inspection and leakage-rate testing requirements.

### Ageing Management Programmes
The driver for implementation of ageing management programmes is coming partly from the need to carry out Periodic Safety Reviews, to confirm on-going safety of reactor operations

late in life. Additional pressures to implement effective ageing management programmes for containments are also coming from plant life extension programmes (60 years operation being a quoted target) and from decommissioning strategies that involve use of the containment as a "safestore" for periods of up to 100 years. These strategies may require the containment to perform its safety functions for significantly longer time periods than initially anticipated.

The CRP's review of international practice showed that many utilities world-wide have already begun implementation of ageing management programmes.

A characteristic of the most effective programmes was the clear definition and documentation of systematic activities aimed at understanding, detecting/ monitoring, and mitigating ageing effects. These programmes generally adopt a reactive approach, in which any effects of ageing are managed (as opposed to modifying operational environments to control the onset of degradation, which would not generally be cost effective). A particular feature of best practice was the routine trending of surveillance and test data to estimate future performance of the containment. This enhances safety by giving confidence that performance remains acceptable until the next planned inspection, and adds value by providing warning of potential problems in sufficient time to permit a planned response to any degradation.

## GENERIC GUIDELINES FOR AGEING MANAGEMENT OF CONTAINMENTS
### Indicators for Assessing Effectiveness of Existing Programmes
Programmes for ageing management of concrete containments would typically be developed as part of a wider initiative for the plant. Guidance on the organisational aspects of a plant ageing management is given in Reference [6]. Contained in this document are suggested indicators for effectiveness, stated as results-oriented criteria. These indicators have been adapted by the CRP, and put into the context of containments. They are summarised in Table 1.

### A Framework For Ageing Management Programmes
The CRP drew on international experience to define a generic framework for ageing management of containments. This seeks to encourage nuclear power plant operators to adopt a systematic approach to ageing management and, in particular, to make best use of information derived from existing maintenance activities (e.g. periodic visual examinations, leak-rate testing and prestressing tendon assessments) to help ensure continued integrity and serviceability of the containment. The proposed approach reflects practice in many countries, including the UK (An overview of UK practice is provided in Reference [7]).

Ageing management programmes for concrete containments have generally focused on managing the effects of degradation (i.e. they are based on periodic inspection or monitoring of the structure, with remedial measures being implemented to deal with any observed degradation before serviceability is lost). This reactive approach is generally cost effective.

The alternative (proactive) approach to ageing management is to control the environment or potential stressors that could lead to degradation. This involves the additional step of controlling and monitoring the operational environment, which adds cost. Such an approach may be appropriate for an inaccessible part of the structure, where detection of degradation would be difficult, or where repair of any degradation would be particularly costly.

Figure 1 shows a schematic of the overall framework proposed by the CRP. A brief summary of each of the key elements is given below; details may be found in Reference 1.

*Understanding* is shown to be central to an optimised Ageing Management Programme. Knowledge of the plant, and of the impact of any potential degradation, is fundamental in making decisions about the inspection requirements, evaluating results, and choosing between remediation options.

Developing the appropriate level of understanding is a continuous process. It builds on plant experience, in particular the performance of both the containment building and contemporaneous structures at the plant. Plant specific knowledge is enhanced by drawing on more general experience of concrete behaviour (from both nuclear and non-nuclear structures).

*Definition of the Ageing Management Programme.* The two fundamental needs are to define an inspection/monitoring programme, and to define criteria against which the results may be judged. This would typically seek to build on existing activities: an interim ageing assessment may be carried out as part of this phase to establish what information is already available (both plant specific and relevant external sources), to provide a general assessment of current condition and to help prioritise subsequent activities.

Some aspects of the programme (e.g., documentation, record keeping, and personnel requirements) will link to the plant's overall strategy for ageing management. The criteria for measuring 'effectiveness' (Table 1) indicate what needs to be considered; Reference 5 gives further guidance.

*Inspection and Monitoring.* The inspection programmes already in place for containments provide a useful starting point for the ageing management programmes. As described above, methods used world-wide are broadly comparable, and predominantly based on a combination of visual inspections, leakage-rate tests, together with checks on tendon loads and corrosion (post-tensioned structures).

The reviews of plant specific performance, or particular features of the design, may highlight additional requirements. Inaccessible concrete areas, for example, place greater reliance on characterisation of condition through indirect monitoring (e.g., quantifying the severity of environmental aggressors). This is often supported by a more detailed assessment of design, construction, and operational history to demonstrate that significant degradation is unlikely.

The inspection and monitoring activities are designed to detect and characterise significant component degradation before fitness-for-service is compromised. Together with an understanding of potential degradation, the results provide a key input to decisions regarding the type and timing of any maintenance actions needed to correct detected degradations

Systematic and effective record keeping is an important part of the inspection process. It is this data that underpins evaluation of the current condition as well as estimates of future performance. The development of electronic databases for collating and retrieving plant data (e.g. operations, inspection and maintenance records) can be helpful, and a suggested approach is included in Reference [8].

*Condition Assessment.* The inspection data provides direct information on current condition, and definition of acceptance criteria against which the results may be judged is considered to be an integral part of a systematic approach to ageing management. Although some acceptance criteria may be found in international design codes [e.g. for crack widths in Reference 9], these

| General Attributes of the AMP |
|---|
| 1. A clearly defined and documented systematic AMP. This documentation includes: |
|    - Overall policy that defines the scope, objectives, activities, and general responsibilities for all relevant organisational units, programmes and activities |
|    - methods and procedures for the conduct of activities aimed at understanding, effectively monitoring, and mitigating ageing of the containment |
|    - performance indicators by which the effectiveness of the AMP can be measured |
| 2. Staffing and resources that are sufficient to accomplish the AMP objectives |
| 3. Personnel involved with implementing the AMP should possess: |
|    - clear understanding of their authority, responsibilities, accountabilities and interfaces with other organisational units and regulatory authorities |
|    - knowledge of relevant ageing phenomena, and their potential impact on the functional capability of the containment and the overall plant safety and reliability |
|    - training and qualifications to perform assigned job functions |
| **General criteria to evaluate the quality of an AMP for containments** |
| 1. Containment's safety and structural functions, and components of the containment that play a key |
| 2. role in maintaining these functions have been identified and documented |
| 3. Pertinent ageing mechanisms that may impact the containment's safety functions have been identified, evaluated and documented |
| 4. Surveillance programme is sufficient to ensure the timely detection of any ageing process (or processes) and its (or their) potential effects |
| 5. Acceptance criteria have been established to determine the need for, type of, and timing of corrective actions. (This may include specified limits for impact of various degradation factors on a component's functional and performance requirements. Although they generally will be somewhat plant specific, design specifications, national codes and standards, regulatory requirements, and industry experience provide sources for development of acceptance criteria.) |
| 6. Methods and criteria have been established to evaluate results obtained from in-service inspection and monitoring that enable determination of whether: |
|    - current condition of the containment complies with acceptance criteria |
|    - estimated future performance, based on trending of historical data or application of service life models in conjunction with reliability based techniques, indicates continued compliance with acceptance criteria. |
|    - ambient environmental parameters and applied loads, together with their trends, are within specified operating limits |
| 7. Options for remedial measures are understood. |
| **General criteria to assess results achieved by an AMP for containments** |
| 1. Actual physical condition of the containment is satisfactory in terms of required safety margins (i.e. integrity and functional capability is retained). |
|    - containment condition and/or functional indicators, provided by surveillance, ISI testing or condition monitoring, and their trends conform to acceptance criteria |
|    - ambient environmental and system parameters (e.g. humidity, temperature and pressure), and their trends are within specified limits |
| 2. Relevant plant safety indicators such as maintenance preventable failures and contribution to containment system unavailability have been satisfactory. |
|    - |

Table 1      Generic Indicators of the Effectiveness of an Ageing Management Programme (AMP) for a Concrete Containment [1]

criteria tend to be limited and often wide ranging. The tendency is to develop plant specific criteria, with a tiered approach to acceptance of an existing condition often being used: inspection results may be used to trigger various levels of response from 'no further action', through more detailed engineering evaluation, to 'urgent remedial action'. The criteria defining the tiers tend to be plant and structure specific.

A single "one-off" inspection of a containment building gives a "snapshot" of its condition at a given point in time. There is, however, considerable value in being able to predict performance from both safety perspectives (demonstrating integrity and functionality until the next planned inspection) and business perspectives (planning any remedial action to avoid prolonged or unplanned outages, supporting life extension decisions).

Estimates of future performance are generally based on extrapolation of results from earlier inspections/ surveys, including comparison with recorded or estimated data at the time of construction and historical data. In the event of degradation being present, an understanding of the processes involved is fundamental as the rate of degradation will vary according to the mechanisms involved (e.g., diffusion or reaction controlled). Further, more frequent inspections may be planned to monitor the actual rate of degradation in the structures.

*Maintenance.* Depending on the degree of degradation and the residual strength of the structure, the objective of a remedial measures programme might be any one, or a combination, of structural, protective, or cosmetic. Options that have been adopted for the containment include (in ascending order of cost):
- Enhanced surveillance to trend progress of deterioration. This is the initial approach adopted as part of the evaluation process during the early stages of degradation and may include a range of non-destructive tests.
- Maintenance and/or operational changes to prevent deterioration from getting worse (if safety margins are acceptable). This might include modified operating conditions (e.g., reducing reactor power, particularly in the shorter term while repairs are planned).
- Local repairs to restore parts of the containment to a satisfactory condition.

### Reviewing the programme
The use of a continuous circle in Figure 1 is deliberate: periodic reviews should be included in the strategy for ageing management. Depending on plant performance, this may lead to either increased or reduced inspection intervals. In addition, continued evolutions in safety thinking and developments in current knowledge relating to both concrete durability and assessment techniques should be incorporated into future versions of the programme.

## FUTURE DEVELOPMENTS IN AGEING MANAGEMENT
Although the CRP reviewed current practice and on-going research, no attempt was made by the CRP to anticipate developments in ageing management practice. This Section of the paper is based on the Author's perspective; it draws on the CRP reviews of ageing management practice and research in both nuclear and non-nuclear industries.

There are two areas where short to medium term developments may be expected to impact on strategies for containment ageing management are:
- increased use of risk based approaches to prioritise inspection and test activities
- the development and application of probabilistic methods to help support strategies.

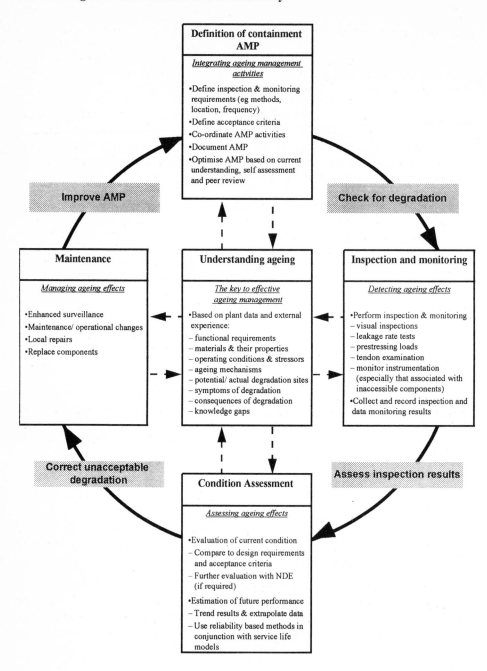

Figure 1    Key Elements of a Concrete Containment Ageing Management Programme (AMP) and Their Interfaces [1]

## Prioritising inspection activities

Generic inspection programmes for containments (e.g. Reference [5]) do not currently give guidance on prioritising inspections for critical locations within the containment. However, a prioritised inspection programme will lead to cost and time savings.

Some utilities are using detailed interim inspection of selected areas/components within the containment to confirm plant condition, so enabling general inspections to be carried out less frequently (at 10–year intervals). The selected locations may include known defects (which are monitored to check activity), or critical locations identified on the basis of ageing assessments. The more detailed inspections also involve routine use of non-destructive techniques to provide quantitative data for trending behaviour of the critical areas.

Optimising surveillance relies on a generic understanding of processes which may result in degradation of concrete structures. This understanding supports identification of the structures that are most susceptible to ageing, the mechanisms involved, and the significance of potential degradation. Optimisation may involve use of formal quantitative ranking systems, or a simple evaluation, to assess the likelihood and consequences of failure on which to base the inspection regimes. In essence, this is a risk based approach. A number of inspection strategies are already based, usually implicitly, on similar approaches. Further moves in this direction might be expected as utilities face increasing pressure to reduce operations and maintenance costs, yet having to do this within the constraints of maintaining existing safety levels and plant availability.

## Probabilistic methods

Probabilistic methods are being developed [e.g. Reference 3] for use as a tool to optimise inspection frequencies based on the significance of ageing to overall plant risk over the lifespan of the containment. These methods take into account the degradation mechanisms, inspection, and remediation measures. They have the advantage of feeding directly into an overall risk assessment for the plant, and of quantitatively assessing the possibility that degradation of civil engineering structures may impact the performance of other mechanical and electrical systems (so called "common cause failures"). This concept has been proven for structural components (e.g. shear walls and beams), but has not yet been applied to complete containment systems. Although not being used routinely today, this work points the way to medium term developments.

## CONCLUSIONS

- There is considerable international variation in the extent to which nuclear power plant operators have implemented ageing management programmes for concrete containments, and other safety related civil structures in their plants.
- A generic framework for systematic ageing management of containments has been developed as part of an IAEA Co-ordinated Research Programme (CRP). This includes criteria for assessing the effectiveness of existing programmes.
- The CRP framework encourages a systematic approach to ageing management and seeks to capitalise on information derived from existing maintenance activities (e.g. periodic visual examinations, leak-rate testing and prestressing tendon assessments) to help ensure continued integrity of the containment. The proposed approach reflects existing UK practice.
- The CRP participants have recommended that the IAEA should work with utilities and regulators to develop this framework into more formalised guidelines.

ACKNOWLEDGEMENTS
This paper is based on the work of all participants in the IAEA Co-ordinated Research Programme: J Pachner (IAEA); C Cragg, C Seni (Canada); V Vydra (Czech Republic); A Ghosh (India); W Heep (Switzerland); D Naus, T Tai (US). Acknowledgements are also due to HSE, for their contribution towards the UK's participation in this IAEA programme.

REFERENCES
1. INTERNATIONAL ATOMIC ENERGY AGENCY, *Working Material: Pilot Study On Management Of Ageing Of Concrete Containment Buildings: Results Of Phase 2,* IAEA/NENS, Limited Distribution, IAEA, Vienna, Austria (1997).

2 INTERNATIONAL ATOMIC ENERGY AGENCY, *Working Material: Summary Results of the Survey on Concrete Containment Ageing,* IAEA/NENS, Limited Distribution, IAEA, Vienna, Austria (1995).

3. NAUS DJ, OLAND CB, ELLINGWOOD BR, *Report of Aging of Nuclear Power Plants Reinforced Concrete Structures,* NUREG/CR-6424, ORNL, Tennessee (1996)

4. ONTARIO HYDRO, *Nuclear Plant Life Assurance, Phase2 Scoping Compilation Report,* NOCS-IR-01512-0021, June 1993

5. AMERICAN SOCIETY OF MECHANICAL ENGINEERS, *Requirements for Class CC Concrete Components of Light-Water Cooled Plants,* Section XI, Subsection IWL, in ASME Boiler and Pressure Vessel code, 1992 edition with Addenda, New York (1995)

6. INTERNATIONAL ATOMIC ENERGY AGENCY, *Implementation and Review of Nuclear Power Plant Ageing Management Programmes,* IAEA Safety Series No. 50, Vienna, Austria (DRAFT 1996).

7. McFARLANE JP, SMITH LM, DAVIES DR, McCLUSKEY DT, *In-service Monitoring of AGR and PWR Nuclear Safety Related Structures,* INucE International Conference on Nuclear Containment, Cambridge, England (Sept 1996)

8. INTERNATIONAL ATOMIC ENERGY AGENCY, *Data Collection and Record Keeping for Management of Nuclear Power Plant Ageing,* IAEA Safety Series No. 50-P-3, Vienna, Austria (1991).

9. AMERICAN CONCRETE INSTITUTE, *ACI 224: Control of Cracking in Concrete Structures,* Detroit (1990)

# Strategies for Extending the Long Term Serviceability of Critical Concrete Structures in Industrial Facilities

DR RENNIE CHADWICK AND DR ROGER MCANOY
Taywood Engineering Ltd., Southall, Middlesex, UK

## SYNOPSIS

This paper presents the authors experiences in working with the owners and operators of process facilities where safety critical concrete structures have been damaged and require assessment, repair or replacement without disruption to normal operations.

There are major operational and technical issues that need to be considered before an effective strategy can be established to extend the service life of, or retrofit these structures. The paper gives examples of some of the analysis required to establish the cause and extent of damage, and residual condition prior to the selection of appropriate options for detailed consideration and design development.

The operational requirement for no disruption (except during periods of planned maintenance) places severe safety and access restraints on possible options. This leads to significant management issues and the need for a far greater degree of planning and co-operation with other disciplines than is encountered in most building and civil engineering rehabilitation works. Guidance is given on some of the common issues encountered.

The paper covers some of the engineering and scientific analysis required, making maximum use of the recent growth of knowledge in a range of relevant technologies. Some of this work is not covered by current codes of practice or industry guidance documents although there are major efforts underway to remedy this shortfall.

Examples have been included in the paper, illustrating the development of a range of practical solutions to the repair and replacement of the foundations of a major petrochemical plant.

## OBJECTIVES

This paper describes the authors experiences of working with plant operators and owners as the Engineer to establish the effective rehabilitation of damaged reinforced concrete elements with minimal operational impact. The three engineering stages of inspection, assessment and rehabilitation are described for a typical investigation and these stages are placed within the framework of an evolving strategy.

## INTRODUCTION

Reinforced concrete is a common construction material for the bases and foundations of industrial process plant and is often used for beams and pipe support structures. Those civil engineering elements would have been designed to the relevant codes of practice current at the time of construction. It would be most unusual for any special consideration to have been given to long term serviceability issues or in the extreme the need for replacement.

*Management of concrete structures for long-term serviceability.* Thomas Telford, London, 1997

Reinforced concrete was often assumed to have a safe and maintenance free working life well in excess of the process equipment design life, although experience demonstrates that this is not universally true [1]. Many process plants are now operating beyond their original design life, typically 20-30 years, and deterioration or damage if left can lead to plant malfunction, pipe leaks or, in the extreme, collapse of a critical element.

There are many reasons why maintenance, repair or retrofitting of the civil engineering elements may be needed. Foundations or support structures may have been damaged through local corrosion or chemical attack. Beams, walls and bases may have moved due to settlement, long term thermal movement or shrinkage, excessive plant loading or the malfunctioning of bearings. Although safety critical damage is unusual in UK, when found it requires rapid action to be taken. There is also the threat of prosecution from regulatory authorities if companies fail to maintain their facilities in good order.

Overseas, especially in the Middle East, ground contamination or wind blown chlorides combine with the higher temperatures to cause very aggressive environmental conditions. Chloride attack may also be prevalent due to the regular soaking of structures by saline water from plant wash down or fire hydrant testing. This environment can result in extensive damage within 10 years. Routine and Principal Inspections of civil engineering structures in process facilities, are uncommon and this lack of inspection and maintenance can allow damage to progress to a condition where structural assessment is required before remediation measures can be established.

## INSPECTION

The most common stimulus to the initiation of an investigation of reinforced concrete condition is visible excessive surface cracking or movement.. A logical approach to the gathering and recording of data is the preferred initial stage in assessing the extent of the problem as this can lead later to significant time savings.

Before any investigations can begin the plant operating procedures will require as a minimum, the inspection team to attend an induction course on safety and to submit comprehensive method statements. Safety and operational procedures will frequently limit the use of NDT equipment, coring and other routinely used plant and equipment, particularly in designated hazardous areas. It is most important that the operator has briefed all relevant internal departments of the scope and impact of the work and the inspection team leader should give a presentation to these departments and invite discussions on any foreseen problems.

A two stage process of investigation allows a non-intrusive general inspection of condition before focusing on areas where more detailed information is required [2]. At the earliest opportunity the inspection should eliminate areas of superficial damage and direct attention to where there is a combination of damage and a potentially significant consequence. Immediate action must be taken if anything is found that threatens the safety of people or plant. Significant findings could be zones where concrete is close to spalling off or if beams have been dislodged. There is also an urgent concern to look for signs of structural movement that could be overstressing any pipework.

It is most important that this inspection stage clearly identifies the cause and extent of damage so that the rate of further damage and any structural risk can be assessed. A judgment of the timing of any intervention works will need to be made at an early stage and there will naturally be  a close scrutiny of any work that is urgent or does not fit into the normal operational timetable.

Figure 1 shows schematically the damage progression of an element. Life prediction models can be used during the assessment stage to predict the consequence of no intervention action, but the data collection demands are higher. Similarly, there is always going to be uncertainty from NDT techniques and in the case of corrosion, some concrete will need to be removed to confirm the actual condition of the reinforcing steel.

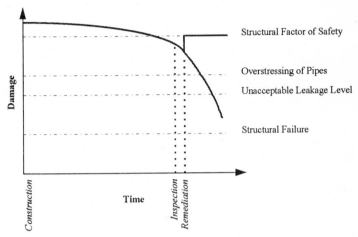

**Figure 1   Schematic illustration of damage progression with time and the influence of repairs**

The subject of inspection of reinforced concrete structures has been covered comprehensively elsewhere [3]. In summary the inspection phase should collect sufficient information to determine the cause and extent of the deterioration; the likely rate of future deterioration; the need for and urgency of repair works and details, such as reinforcement layout, details and loading arrangements, sufficient to complete the necessary structural assessment.

## ASSESSMENT

It is recognised that structural assessment requires a different approach to the design of new works [4]. There is a wealth of knowledge in the public domain [5, 6], but very little definitive guidance in codes of practice. A specialist structural engineer with knowledge of rehabilitation techniques should be used.

However, there are still strategic issues which must be cleared with the operator. One key issue is the design basis e.g. which codes of practice should apply and what safety factors should be applied. Those decisions lead to a different selection of load cases (for example, seismic loading) and the use of either an elastic or a limit state analysis. Normally the safety factors required are equivalent to those of the original design taking into account actual values for material strength and loads.

The design basis may require third party approval, as part of a plant or company safety procedures. Some process owners have their own group of civil engineers as these advisors. The lack of codes and definitive guidance documents can cause difficulties when agreeing the design basis. Time and effort is required to mutually agree this critical document. The results of the assessment and the need/selection/cost/timing of rehabilitation can be influenced significantly by these early decisions.

Caution is required in assessing the structural impact of remediation as invasive methods can cause temporary overloading or even instability. It is relatively easy to overlook a critical potential failure mechanism during repair and either the method must be defined by the assessor or a check carried out on a contractors detailed method statement plus strict instructions given that there can be no variations without clearance.

If repair is not immediately a safety critical issue, the timing of rehabilitation becomes a

Client decision and the relatively new science of deterioration prediction over time is now reliable enough to assist with this decision [7].

To summarise, the assessment phase must cover at least the following aspects:

**Drawing review for details of construction** - to confirm details such as the structural form, reinforcement details, codes used for design, detailing practices, materials used and the sequence of construction.

**Survey Data review** - to compare actual conditions of cover, dimensions, material properties and loads with those used in the original design.

**Assessment of actual capacity versus required capacity** - this may require the production of calculations to identify global stability, governing load cases, N-M curves for column capacity, identification of actual load paths and estimation of current factors of safety.

**Verification of deterioration mechanism(s)** - to identify the risk of damage propagating and hence estimate the range of residual life of the structure before intervention is required.

The output of the assessment and inspection phases is a recommendation on the need, urgency and scope of remedial works. This will essentially form the design brief and as such it should be discussed and agreed with the client stakeholders prior to the start of design of the remedial works.

## REHABILITATION APPROACH

Currently, there are no British Standards that adequately cover the repair of damaged structures. There are a number of guidance documents available from organizations such as the Concrete Society and FIP [9]. However, these documents were produced in the early to mid 1980's and do not reflect current technologies. The most recent guide is a draft CEN code of practice that is at the consultation stage, prEN 1504-9:1995 Part 9 'General principles for the use of products and systems'. Although these documents provide some guidance in the principles they do not offer much in the way of practical examples and therefore the engineering team often have to rely on professional experience and published case histories.

The primary objectives of any repair to process plant support structures is to restore the structure to a known structural capacity in excess of that required to fulfill its purpose and a maintainable condition.

### Concept Design

It is common to find that most foundation or support structures within an operating facility are of a similar design or geometry, e.g. tower type structures are often founded on octagonal pads with a central octagonal plinth, the dimensions of the pad and plinth are sized to match the dimensions of the tower and the resulting imposed loads. Standardisation of structure types can be used to rationalise the design of remedial works to the extent that a generic design solution can be developed which can then be either 'stretched' or 'shrunk' to fit other structures of similar geometry.

The cause and extent of the deterioration identified during the inspection phase must also be addressed when developing the remedial strategy. If the problem is primarily caused by conditions in the ground (e.g. chloride bearing ground water) then it is likely that the remedial strategy will need to address the whole facility. However, if the problem is dominated by operating conditions, such as leaking pipes or salt water wash down, then the strategy may need to be focused on discrete areas of the facility, where these activities occur frequently.

For foundations to tower type structures the wind and test loads normally dominate and in this case the foundation must distribute the axial loads and provide a resistance to overturning without exceeding the bearing capacity of the ground, Figure 2

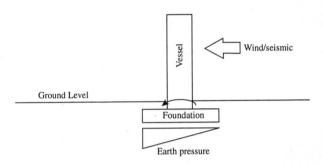

**Figure 2. Schematic representation of primary loads on a tower foundation structure.**

In this case, if the corrosion of reinforcement has developed as a result of chlorides in the ground, then the reinforcement in the bottom face of the foundation is at high risk but is inaccessible for inspection and assessment. Judgments about its contribution to current capacity must therefore be based on the condition of accessible areas. Having decided that some intervention is necessary the next step is to review options and identify the preferred approach. Options would normally include; direct replacement; additional structural elements; structural redundancy; cathodic protection.

It is outside the scope of this paper to review in detail each of these options as the project specific details will tend to dominate the relative pro's and con's. However, any design must take account of the technical requirements and function of the structure and balance these against the constraints imposed by the operation of the facility.

### Replacement

The simplest and cheapest approach would be to demolish the existing structure and replace it with a suitably designed and specified new foundation. This would mean either interrupting the operation of plant or carrying out the work within a planned plant outage period both of which have major implications. In either case the process plant must be supported during the demolition phase and this would necessitate the construction of temporary works capable of transferring the loads from the old pad and back onto the new pad without overstressing the attached pipework and services. As a result these temporary works are often more complex than the permanent works and, due to space restrictions are different for each structure, contradicting the generic approach described earlier. Therefore, a more efficient solution can be based on one, or a combination, of the other options.

### Additional Structural Elements

Bracing of tower structures would appear to be a cheap and simple solution as in principle it removes the need for the foundation to resist wind forces and carry axial loads only. In practice the option is limited due to the lack of space around the tower; the bracing forces on the tower structure itself and the difference in stiffness of the bracing system, the tower and the foundation with respect to allowable pipe movements. This option can be pursued for individual towers but is not suited for development as a generic solution. For other structure types, such as pedestals, the option is more viable as the bracing can be designed to act in compression and can be connected to the foundation rather than the process plant.

### Structural Redundancy

Options which concentrate on the existing foundation open up a range of possibilities, which can either add structural elements which act in concert with the original structure, or impose a new structure which attracts load into it as the original structure deteriorates. In the case of our example structure it is possible to add a prestressed belt around the existing pad to remove all of the tensile stress from the bottom face, Figure 3. Alternatively, an additional ring beam around the pedestal section can be used to make the pad section redundant, Figure 4.

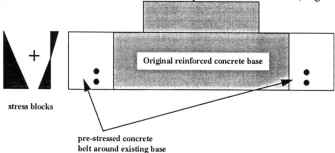

**Figure 3. Schematic representation of a prestressed belt strengthening approach**

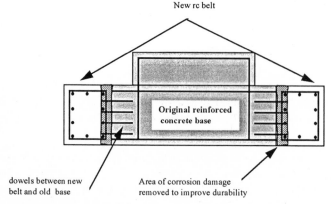

**Figure 4. Schematic representation of a ring beam strengthening approach**

Both of these approaches are technically feasible and either could be designed and detailed in such a way that it could be constructed within an operating facility. They have the additional benefit that the principle can be applied to structures of the same geometry but with different dimensions and loads. However the use of prestressing requires specialist contracting expertise and imposes an additional level of safety and risk management, either of which may raise difficulties when working in a operating facility.

**Detailed Design**

Detailed design of the remedial works must incorporate the structural and durability aspects required for the structure to perform satisfactorily. This may require the use of high performance concretes, protective coatings, corrosion resistant reinforcement, advanced composites and electrochemical techniques.

The engineering team must take into account several aspects which are peculiar to this type of project, including; load paths before during and after repair; durability design of remedial works; other works (e.g. fixing source of leaks); temporary works and relocation of services, the maintenance requirements and access required to the plant supported by the foundation (e.g. heat, radiation, noise, dust, water, power, light etc.)

The new structure must also be detailed to ensure that no incompatibilities are built in which may reduce the service life below the required level. The area of highest risk is usually the interface between the old and new materials[8]. It is important to include all disciplines in the project team so that structural , materials and construction issues are addressed. It is unusual to find adequate expertise in all three fields residing in one individual so this often results in a process of design development with periodic project team review, including client stakeholders. The review process must be documented so that the logic behind decisions is understood and may be re-visited later if changes need to be made. This process is not significantly different from good design practice but the technical content is and for this reason it is important to document the design development comprehensively.

**Implementation**

Having invested time and effort in developing the design it must be implemented efficiently. Conventional procurement strategies may not be appropriate and some thought must be devoted to identifying, in conjunction with the client stakeholders, the most effective means of realising the planned work. Clear and concise contract documentation must reflect the important aspects of the design. The technical specification will often contain more detailed information than is usual on the allowable materials and methods together with a clearly defined set of 'hold' points and a robust QA/QC system which, in itself, must be consistent with the level of supervision anticipated by the project team and the facilities permi to work system.

**DEVELOPMENT OF AN EFFECTIVE ENGINEERING STRATEGY**

From the preceding sections it is clear that the success of a remediation scheme is dependent on a large number of variables. If a scheme is based on incorrect assumptions or fails to take into account the needs of one of the parties involved then there is a high risk of failure, duplication of effort and poor value for money. Because the work of the Engineer must be undertaken within the confines of an operating facility it is essential that constructive dialogue is established between the Engineer and the Client at the beginning and maintained throughout the project.

Figure 5 summarises the main elements of effort in the development of a remediation strategy and shows the need for inputs from both the Engineer and the Client. The detail involved in each stage is project specific and therefore impossible to cover comprehensively in this paper.

There are however, several points which are worthy of note.

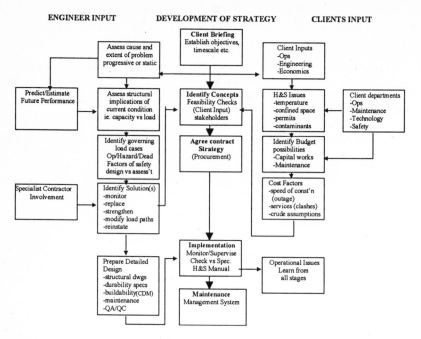

**Figure 5   A flow diagram of the development of an engineering strategy showing the inputs from the Engineering and Client teams**

The initial briefing may be more than a single meeting as the Client may need to internally review the consequences of embarking on a remediation strategy.  It is absolutely imperative that at this stage all of the departments, or stakeholders, within the Client organisation are identified and as far as is practicable, involved in the development of the remedial works.

Input from the Client team can normally be grouped into three areas, engineering, operations and economics.  The level of detail of input in each area will depend on the relative sizes of the departments involved and the degree of criticality of the process plant supported by the civil structures.  The more important the plant, the greater the level of attention it will attract from the Clients team.  An understanding of the Clients business must also be developed by the Engineering team as this will facilitate the design and implementation of the remedial works.

The process of identifying and briefing the key stakeholders can pay dividends in terms of smoother and shorter approval times.  It is also useful to identify with them a set of success criteria against which the project will be judged.  Often, within an operating facility, these will be remote from the technical detail of the remedial works but they will reflect the potential impact of the work on the operation of the facility, (for example, the most important criteria may be containment of hazardous materials.  These need to be identified and reviewed throughout the project as they will form the basis of the brief to the Engineering team working on the assessment, design and implementation phases of the project.  It is likely that these criteria will evolve during the life of the project and the strategy must allow for changes to be agreed and communicated to the whole of the project team.

Identification of feasible concepts for solving the existing problems also requires input from the Client stakeholders as in most cases the remediation works will involve significant work activities to be carried out within the operating facility. In some cases the activities proposed will be outside the scope of existing work permit systems and therefore new operating procedures and safety guidelines will need to be developed. These will have a time and cost implication and therefore may alter the selection of a concept scheme. Availability of specialist contractors should also be considered, particularly when working outside the UK or in remote locations.

Communication between the Engineering team and the stakeholders will improve the level of common knowledge of feasible schemes and approaches with resulting improvements in the development of remedial works. This becomes corporate project knowledge and must be documented in a controlled manner, often in the project quality plan or the design manual for the project.

The design stage may be undertaken remote from the client team, provided that all constraints and methods of complying with them are understood. Experience has shown that it is normally beneficial to include review sessions with the stakeholders once outline designs are identified and again when the detailed designs are 85-95% complete. This will allow the most effective level of interaction between the Engineering team and the stakeholders. It is also useful to consider input from specialist contractors at this stage, particularly if unusual operating conditions or work sequences are required to effect the works. A practical appreciation of the outline design on the part of the designer is also invaluable. This stage is where there is the greatest potential for building in problems with subsequent work and in our experience, time and money invested here saves on rectification of errors once work has commenced. Most process operators are familiar with this approach as outage works are planned in great detail in advance to the same end, minimising loss of operating time.

The selection of a procurement strategy will depend on the finance options available to the client and their in-house approach to procurement. The most productive form of contract is based on the principle of shared risk and reward, or partnering. This recognises that the operating environment is unusual and that a primary success criteria is no loss of production. Forms of contract which may be suitable are the IChemE standard forms and the New Engineering Contract.

Implementation of the works introduces a third party to the project team, the contractor. Success at this stage again depends on clear and open lines of communication between the parties involved and a common understanding and ownership of the objectives of the project. The structure of the QA/QC system developed during the design stage will also have an impact on the progress of the work and it can make a positive contribution provided that all parties understand and agree on the objectives.

## ACKNOWLEDGMENTS
The authors would like to thank the Directors of Taywood Engineering Ltd for permission to publish this paper the clients with whom we have worked in developing the approach covered in this paper.

## REFERENCES

1. Wallbank, E.J., 'The performance of concrete in bridges.', HMSO, London, 1989.

2. Browne, R.D., Broomfield, J.P., McAnoy, R., McLeish, A. & Robery, P., 'Diagnosis and repair of marine structures, towards a unified approach.', Proc. Marine Concrete '86, The Concrete Society, pp. 321-332, 1986

3. Browne, R.D., 'Durability of reinforced concrete structures.', Proc. Pacific Concrete Conference, vol. 3, pp. 847-886, New Zealand Concrete Society, 1988.

4. BA 51/95 The assessment of concrete structures affected by steel corrosion., Department of Transport, 1995.

5. Baldwin, M.I. and Clark, L.A., 'The assessment of reinforcing bars with inadequate anchorage.', Mag. Conc. Res., 47, No. 171, June, 1995.

6. Clark. L.A., 'Concrete bridge assessment.', Proc. Bridge Modification 2, Thomas Telford, London, 1997.

7. Bamforth, P.B., 'Predicting the risk of reinforcement corrosion in marine structures.', Proc. 3rd CANMET/ACI conf., Performance of Concrete in Marine Environments, New Brunswick, Canada, 1996

8. Chadwick, R., 'Performance of concrete repair materials as corrosion protection for reinforcement.', Ph.D., Surrey University, 1993.

9. 'Repair of concrete damaged by reinforcement corrosion', Concrete Society Technical Report No. 26, 1986.

# Management of Railtrack for Serviceability and the Future

KIM TEAGER CEng MICE
Civil Engineer, Standards, Railtrack PLC

## SYNOPSIS
This paper describes Railtracks management of structures for serviceability and the future.

The paper deals with the financial management of its portfolio of structures, the Asset Maintenance Plan, and the management controls used to ensure safety and economic operation of that portfolio. Management controls described are those for structures examination, assessment, design and construction.

## OBJECTIVES
The objectives of the paper are to outline

- a robust system, which if operated by competent engineers will deliver safe and cost effective management of structures.
- to identify the need for the concrete industry to assist in the good management of structures through the provision of reliable performance based predictive tools

## RAILTRACK
Created as a result of the privatisation of British Rail (BR), Railtrack is the owner, operator and maintainer of rail infrastructure in England, Scotland and Wales. The company took responsibility for the infrastructure during April 1994 (though still wholly owned by the Government) and was privatised through a Stock Market Flotation during 1996. The commercial activities of the company are regulated by the Office of the Rail Regulator which engineering and rail operations are monitored by Her Majesty's Railway Inspectorate.

## ASSET MAINTENANCE PLAN
In order that the rigours of floating the company on the stock market could be satisfied it was necessary to understand the infrastructure maintenance and renewal need over a period of ten years. BR had no strategic plan for the infrastructure therefore it was necessary to develop one from first principles.

- The Asset maintenance Plan (AMP) was required to deliver, for civil engineering and property assets, an assessment of the work volume and price for maintenance and renewal necessary to ensure that steady state condition is maintained throughout the period of the plan. The AMP was not intended to make any assessment on investment to deliver an improvement, or change to the infrastructure. Steady state condition is difficult to define,

*Management of concrete structures for long-term serviceability.* Thomas Telford, London, 1997

however for the purposes of the AMP steady state is defined as ensuring that the infrastructure is maintained at the:

- Size
- Capacity
- Linespeeds
- Reliability

in place during April 1994, or as defined in track access agreements with Railtracks customers the Train Operating Companies.

The AMP further defined steady state as being the maintenance standard necessary to meet:

- Relevant statutory obligations
- Railway Group Standards
- Good engineering practice

For each structure type Railtrack then defined a maintenance policy. This providing further bench marks for the AMP exercise. In the case of Bridges and the policy is as follows:

It is Railtrack's policy to maintain its bridges in a condition fit for purposes:

- To minimise the risk of total or partial structural failure through compliance with national legislation, Railway Group Standards, Railtrack Line Standards for safety and quality, and through good engineering practice.
- To maintain route carrying capacities for axle weights, speeds and gross annual tonnages to deliver Railtracks obligations to its customers under track access agreements.
- To constantly seek to identify and implement best practice in service delivery in support of safety and commercial objectives.

Thereby achieving safe and cost effective operation of the infrastructure.

It will be noted that there is no attempt to define pure engineering criteria for maintenance standards. The phrase 'fit for purpose' is deliberately used, further discussion of the significance of the phrase will be seen later in this paper.

## SYSTEM ENHANCEMENT.
Enhancements to the system are not covered within the AMP. These are separately funded investment items that must have their own business case. Obviously with commercial benefit to Railtrack.

## STRUCTURES MANAGEMENT
There are many complex and interrelated activities that make up the structures management life cycle. These may be summarised as the management control of:

- Examination
- Assessment
- Design
- Construction

Figure1. shows the interrelationship of these activities. It can be seen that there are two basic drivers to the process, routine management and the management of change. It is important to understand the successful management of structures depends upon all of the activities being undertaken with an awareness of the needs of the others.

## Management Control

Management control is at the heart of managing any portfolio of assets. Competent staff areemployed, competency is defined in terms of both qualifications and experience. Their responsibilities are defined in writing. Railtrack does not employ a direct labour force, all its physical activities are undertaken through contractors. Again only competent contractors are employed, competencies are defined and the procurement process is focused to ensure that responsibilities are defined through the contracts. Areas of competence include the management of:

- Records
- Examination process
- Assessment processes
- Risks associated with bridge strikes
- Risks associated with scour and flooding
- The management of contractors
- Risks associated with maintenance and renewal work.

## STRUCTURES EXAMINATION PROCESS

Railtrack operates three levels of routine examination.

### Route Observations

All staff and contractors on or about the railway are required to be vigilant for potential risks. This requirement is a contractual commitment with the Infrastructure maintenance contractor.

### Visual Examinations

All significant structures receive an annual examination to observe significant deterioration and to monitor known major defects.

### Detail Examination

All significant structures receive, typically, a six yearly examination during which full access to the bridge is gained and a detailed report is made. It is usually, but not always, from this examination that decisions are made regarding actions necessary to maintain the continued safe operation of the structure.

Arising from any examination reports the zone manager may take one or more to the following actions:

- Do nothing (no concerns)
- Request assessment (condition gives rise to concern over capacity)
- Request more frequent examination (classify as a sensitive structure) in order to monitor deterioration.
- Apply immediate restriction to the bridge speed and weight restrictions or closure are options)
- Initiate immediate work (propping, strengthening)

(See figure1)

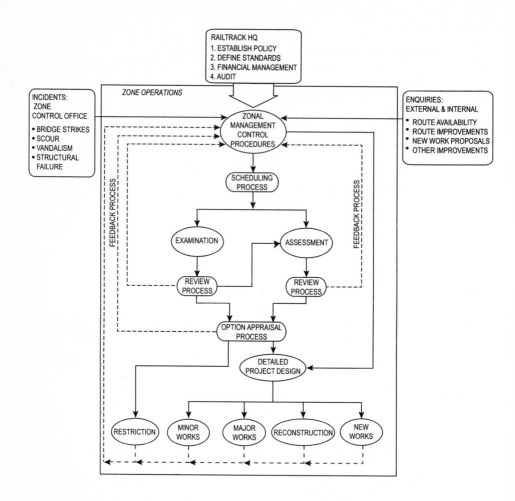

**Figure 1. Inter-relationship of Examination, Assessment, Design and Construction**

## STRUCTURES ASSESSMENT PROCESS
Railtrack is currently using the bridge assessment code inherited from BR. This is based on permissible stress analysis and the now deleted British Standard BS 253. No formal assessment codes exist for other types of structures. A new bridge assessment code is proposed based on limit state analysis and BS 5400. However much work is needed to ensure that the new code can deliver the level of safety currently achieved in an affordable manner. The experience of Local Authorities implementing the highway bridges assessment code is an important lesson to learn.

The assessment process is controlled through series of stages:

- approval in principle of assessment
- Category for check
- Certification of assessment and check

### *Approval in Principle of Assessment.*
Before any assessment is undertaken (usually by a consulting engineer) a suitably competent Railtrack engineer will agree the type of analysis to be undertaken. This process is known as 'Approval Principle', (AIP). Any deviation of current standards or methods of analysis must be identified and agreed. It is through this process that Railtrack satisfies itself that it, as client and the party ultimately responsible for the safety of the infrastructure, is discharging its duties diligently.

### *Category for Check*
All calculations must be accompanied by a suitable check certificate. The level of check is dependant upon the complexity of the assessment:

- Category 1 - simply, supported, square span and standard analysis. Checked by the team undertaking the assessment.

- Category 2 - Skew or continuous structure or minor deviation from standards. Checked by independent engineers, but can be undertaken in-house.

- Category 3 - Complex analytical techniques, complex structure or major deviation fro standards. Checked by organisation external to the assessing organisation.

### *Certificate of Assessment and Check*
All completed assessments must be accompanied by a certificate confirming compliance to the AIP form and that a relevant check has been undertaken.

Once the results of an assessment are known the Railtrack manager has a number of possible actions open to him:

- Do nothing (no concerns)
- Request more frequent examination (classify as a sensitive structure) in order to monitor deterioration.
- Apply immediate restriction to the bridge (speed and weight restrictions or closure are options)

♦ Initiate immediate work (propping, strengthening

♦ Plan for maintenance, strengthening or renewal of the structure whole maintaining current loading.

### Assessment for Scour.

All bridges identified as being t a risk from scour are assessed to a standard prioritisation process. High and medium priority bridges are subject to rigorous hydrological assessment and physical works are based on that assessment.

### Assessment for risk from Bridge Strikes.

Railtrack routinely monitors all its bridge strikes, this assists in identifying problem sites. This analysis together with other risk based analytical techniques allows Railtrack to undertake preventative works on critical bridges.

### Railtrack owned Public Highway Bridges.

Railtrack owned Public Highway Bridges are assessed to the relevant Department of Transport standards.

## STRUCTURES WORKS DESIGN PROCEDURES.

Once the decision has been made to undertake physical works Railtrack implements a number of controls to ensure that proper consideration is given to:

♦ Structural adequacy

♦ Material and workmanship

♦ Construction, future maintenance and decommissioning

♦ Compatibility with existing infrastructure

♦ Railway operation safety

The control measures are similar to those described above for assessment calculations, through with one important addition. These are:

♦ Approval in principle of design

♦ Category for check

♦ Certification of assessment and check

♦ HMRI approval for new works

## MANAGEMENT OF RAILTRACK STRUCTURES FOR SERVICEABILITY AND THE FUTURE

Assuming that all the processes described in this paper are complied with Railtrack will have a safe and durable asset portfolio. The question that remains unanswered is, at what cost, and can the industry afford it. It should not be forgotten that Railtrack's costs are reflected within the price of passengers ticket. Simple compliance with standards for the construction of new bridges is not an affordable way of managing structures.

It is therefore necessary to return to the definition of maintaining assets 'fit for purpose'. Using the example of a bridge, fit for purpose means:

♦ Adequate to carry loading required from it

- maintenance or renewal intervention levels based on the optimisation of the following criteria:
  - ◊ Strategic importance
  - ◊ Location
  - ◊ whole life costs of the bridge and commercial value of the route it carries.

It can be seen that in following this principle similar structures in different locations could be operated in varying conditions. An important issue for the concrete industry to grasp is the need to provide engineers with information on the consequences of common defects found in structures. Information on rates of deterioration, consequential damage, repair options and longevity of repair etc., in order that cost effective management decisions can be made, using robust risk and financial assessment.